Reinforced and Prestressed Masonry

Concrete Design and Construction Series

SERIES EDITORS

PROFESSOR F. K. KONG
University of Newcastle upon Tyne

EMERITUS PROFESSOR R. H. EVANS CBE
University of Leeds

OTHER TITLES IN THE SERIES

Concrete Radiation Shielding: Nuclear Physics, Concrete Properties and Construction *by M. F. Kaplan*

Quality in Precast Concrete: Design — Production — Supervision *by John G. Richardson*

Reinforced and Prestressed Masonry

EDITED BY

Arnold W. Hendry
Emeritus Professor of Civil Engineering
University of Edinburgh

Copublished in the United States with
John Wiley & Sons, Inc., New York

Longman Scientific & Technical,
Longman Group UK Limited,
Longman House, Burnt Mill, Harlow,
Essex CM20 2JE, England
and Associated Companies throughout the world.

Copublished in the United States with
John Wiley & Sons, Inc., 605 Third Avenue, New York, NY 10158

© Longman Group UK Limited 1991

First published 1991

British Library Cataloguing in Publication Data
Reinforced and prestressed masonry
  1. Concrete structural components
  I. Hendry, A. W. (Arnold William) II. Series
  624.1834

  ISBN 0-582-05917-8

Library of Congress Cataloging-in-Publication Data
Reinforced and prestressed masonry / edited by Arnold W. Hendry.
       p. cm. -- (Concrete design and construction series.)
    Includes bibliographical references and index.
    ISBN 0-470-21684-0
    1. Reinforced masonry. 2. Prestressed masonry. I. Hendry, A. W.
  (Arnold W.), 1921−   . II. Series.
  TA670.R43   1991
  624.1'83412--dc20   90-13395
                                                                        CIP

Set in 10/12 pt Times.
Printed and Bound in Great Britain
at the Bath Press, Avon

Contents

Preface

Reinforced masonry has found practical application for many years, particularly in areas subject to earthquakes. Prestressed masonry has been developed much more recently and so far has been used only to a limited extent, mostly in the UK. Interest in the design of these forms of construction and appreciation of their potential have emerged in recent years, to some extent, at least, handicapped by the absence of relevant codes of practice. Such a code, however, was published in the UK in 1985 and others are currently in preparation. A considerable amount of research has been carried out on both reinforced and prestressed masonry so that the scene is set for a substantial increase in the application of these forms of construction.

The time appeared ripe, therefore, to assemble state-of-the-art reviews of key aspects of reinforced and prestressed masonry construction in a form that would be useful to designers and research workers in any country. Each chapter in this book has therefore been written by an author who has had considerable experience in the particular subject of his contribution. Reference is made to national codes of practice where relevant, but the intention has been to discuss basic principles and their application to design practice rather than to produce a design guide which would necessarily have to relate closely to a particular code and to methods of construction in the country of origin.

The authors hope that this will contribute to the wider application of the forms of construction discussed in the interests of producing buildings and structures which will take advantage of the recognized merits of masonry in terms of appearance, durability and economy.

A. W. Hendry
Edinburgh, December 1989

Acknowledgements

In writing the several chapters of this book the authors have drawn on a very large number of publications by research workers, practising engineers and architects throughout the world. Sources of information and references are indicated throughout the text and the authors acknowledge their indebtedness to all who have contributed to the literature on reinforced and prestressed masonry. In particular, permission has been granted to reproduce material by The Institution of Civil Engineers, The Institution of Structural Engineers The British Masonry Society, Macmillan Education Ltd, Expanded Metal Company Ltd, McCalls Special Products Ltd, VSL International, The Aggregate Concrete Block Association and The Brick Development Association.

We are grateful to the following for permission to reproduce copyright material:

British Research Establishment, UK for fig. 5 by R. H. Wood pp. 381−411 of the *Proceedings of the Institution of Civil Engineers* Part 2 (1978), reproduced by permission of the Controller, HMSO (Crown Copyright); the Expanded Metal Company Ltd for figures based on figs 1.3 and 1.4; Macmillan Publishers Ltd for figs 4.16, 4.17 and 4.18 by A. W. Hendry from *Structural Brickwork* (1981); New Zealand National Society for Earthquake Engineering and the author for fig. 4 by M. J. N. Priestley from p. 177 of the *Bulletin of the New Zealand National Society for Earthquake Engineering* Vol. 7, No. 4 (1974).

Notation

A = cross-sectional area
A_b = effective cross-sectional area of wall
A_e = effective aspect ratio of shear wall
A_m = cross-sectional area of masonry
A_{ps} = area of prestressing tendons
A_s = area of tension reinforcement
A_{st} = total area of flexural reinforcement
A_{sv} = shear steel area
A_v = area of vertical reinforcement in shear wall
AY = first moment of area
a = deflection
a_m = deflection due to moment
a_v = shear span; deflection due to shear
B = effective width of masonry or web spacing; non-dimensional parameter related to bending moment
B_x, B_y = non-dimensional parameters representing M_x and M_y respectively
b = width of beam
b_w = width of web
D = overall depth of wall
d = effective depth
d_1, d_2 = concrete cover to centroid of A_{s1} and A_{s2} respectively
d_b = bar diameter
d_c = depth of masonry in compression
E = modulus of elasticity
E_m = modulus of elasticity of masonry
E_s = modulus of elasticity of steel
e = base of Napierian logarithms
e = eccentricity
e_{add} = increased eccentricity
e_s = eccentricity of prestress

F_m = compressive strength of confined masonry

f = stress

f_{1t} = masonry stress at transfer (bottom of beam or back of wall)

f_{2t} = masonry stress at transfer (top of beam or front of wall)

f_{1s} = masonry stress at service (bottom of beam or back of wall)

f_{2s} = masonry stress at service (top of beam or front of wall)

f_{at} = average masonry stress at transfer

f_B = brick strength

f_b = bending strength of prestressed masonry perpendicular to bed joints

f_c = principal compressive stress in masonry

f_{cr} = prestress at centroid of section at diagonal cracking load for wall cracked in flexure

f_{cs} = allowable masonry compressive stress at service

f_{ct} = allowable compressive stress at transfer

f_e = effective prestress in tendon

f_i = initial transfer

f_k = characteristic compressive strength of masonry

f_{kh} = design bending strength of prestressed masonry perpendicular to bed joints

f_{kt} = strength of masonry at transfer

f_{kx} = characteristic flexural tensile strength of masonry perpendicular to the bed joints

f_m = masonry compressive strength or permissible stress

f_{mi} = masonry stress at tendon level at transfer

f_n = normal compressive stress

f_p = stress due to prestress at centroid of section

f_{pb} = tensile stress in tendon at ultimate limit state

f_{pj} = stress in tendon at jacking end

f_{ps} = net vertical prestress on leaf

f_{pu} = characteristic tensile strength of tendon

f_{px} = stress at distance x from jacking end

f_s = total stress in tendon at ultimate; permissible tensile stress in steel

f_{sb} = stress associated with tendon strain ϵ_{sb}

f_{sv} = shear strength with vertical bars

f_t = diagonal tensile strength of masonry

f_{ts} = allowable masonry tensile stress at service

f_{tt} = allowable masonry tensile stress at transfer

f_v = shear strength without shear steel

f_y = characteristic tensile strength of steel
G_m = shear modulus of masonry
H = overall depth of beam or column section
h = height of wall
h_b = beam depth
h_c = height of column in framed building; joint width
h_{ef} = effective height of column
h_o = height of window opening in framed building
I = second moment of area
I_c = second moment of area of cracked section
I_n = second moment of area of wall n
I_u = second moment of area of uncracked section
j = lever arm of shear force couple across tie
jd = lever arm
k = coefficient depending on type of duct
k_1, k_2, k_3 = characteristic ratios of stress block
L = non-dimensional parameter related to axial load
l = beam length
l_n = clear span between column faces
l_w = wall length
M = applied bending moment; total floor area
M_a = increased moment
M_B = moment at top of column
M_c = serviceability moment of resistance of wall
M_{cr} = cracking moment for wall in flexure
M_d = design moment
M_{d+L} = bending moment due to dead and live load
M_h = horizontal moment of resistance of flange
M_i = bending moment due to self-weight
M_m = moment in column at level of top of infill wall
M_r = moment at top of column; torsional moment
M_s = bending moment at serviceability limit state
M_T = torsional moment
M_u = bending moment at ultimate limit state
M_x = design moment about x-axis
M_{x^1} = effective uniaxial design moment about x-axis
M_y = design moment about y-axis
M_{y^1} = effective uniaxial design moment about y-axis
m = bending moment to cause hinges in tie; modular ratio
m_t = plastic moment of resistance of tie
N = compressive axial load
N_d = design axial load
N_s = axial load at serviceability limit state
N_{sw} = self-weight

N_u = axial load at ultimate limit state
N_{uz} = capacity of column section under axial compression
P = prestressing force
P_{cr} = force in tendon at moment M_{cr}
P_e = effective prestressing force
P_y, P_u = racking load on shear wall at first yield and ultimate, respectively
r = width of tie
$1/r$ = curvature
S = standard deviation; non-dimensional parameter related to area of reinforcement
s = spacing of ties or reinforcing bars
t = overall depth of column; thickness of wall; thickness of tie
t_f = flange thickness
t_w = thickness of wall resisting shear
V = shear force
V_A = actual shear force
V_c = diagonal cracking strength
V_{cr} = shear force to give diagonal cracking in wall cracked in flexure
V_D = maximum design shear force on a shear wall
V_F = dependable shear strength of a shear wall
V_{jh} = horizontal joint shear
V_N = load resisted by a shear wall
V_{sh} = shear on a joint
V_t = shear force acting on a tie
v = shear stress
v_0 = shear strength of unit/mortar joint at zero normal stress
v_c = permissible shear stress for wall uncracked in flexure
v_{cr} = permissible shear stress for wall cracked in flexure
v_k = characteristic shear strength
v_s = shear stress at moment causing flexural cracking
W_w = total vertical load on beam
w = uniformly distributed load
x = neutral axis depth; distance from jacking end
y_n = distance of wall from shear centre
Z = section modulus
Z_1 = section modulus referred to bottom of beam or back of wall

Z_2 = section modulus referred to top of beam or front of wall

z = section modulus for flange in horizontal bending

α = prestress loss ratio; bond factor

α_e = modular ratio E_s/E_m

α_s = shear deformation coefficient

β = capacity reduction factor for axial load

γ_f = partial safety factor for load

γ_{fd} = partial safety factor for dead load

γ_{fw} = partial safety factor for wind load

γ_m = partial safety factor for material strength

γ_{mm} = partial safety factor for masonry strength

γ_{ms} = partial safety factor for steel strength

Δf_{ms} = corresponding prestress in masonry stress at tendon level

Δf_s = loss of prestress in tendons at transfer

Δf_{sc} = loss of prestress due to creep

Δf_{ss} = loss of prestress in tendon

ϵ_{bt} = masonry strain due to bending

ϵ_{ma} = masonry strain due to applied load

ϵ_{mp} = masonry strain due to prestress

ϵ_{ms} = masonry shrinkage strain

ϵ_{mu} = ultimate compressive strain

ϵ_{pa} = strain in prestressing tendon due to applied load

ϵ_{pb} = strain in prestressing tendon at ultimate limit state

ϵ_{pe} = strain in tendons due to effective prestress

ϵ_{sb} = tendon strain due to bending

ϵ_u = masonry ultimate strain

ϵ_x = strain in the x-direction

ϵ_y = steel strain at yield point

ϵ_1, ϵ_2 = compressive strain in column reinforcement A_{s1} and A_{s2} respectively

ϕ = creep factor

ϕ_f = flexural strength reduction factor

ϕ_o = strength enhancement factor allowing for strain hardening

ϕ_s = strength reduction factor for shear

ϕ_u = ultimate curvature of shear wall

ϕ_y = curvature at base of shear wall at first yield

μ = friction coefficient; ductility factor

ρ = steel ratio

ρ_s = volumetric ratio of confinement steel

θ = angle of inclination of f to bed joint

ω_v = shear amplification factor

1 Development and Applications of Reinforced and Prestressed Masonry

Donald Foster, consultant architect

Development of Reinforced Masonry

Review of Research in Reinforced Brick Masonry

Reinforced masonry (r.m.) is not new. Reinforced brick masonry (r.b.m.) preceded reinforced concrete (r.c.) — indeed the protagonists of r.c. quoted earlier uses of reinforced brick (r.b.) in support of their aims, around the last decades of the nineteenth century. According to Filippi,[1.1] from whose record much of the following history is derived, Marc Isambard Brunel, father of the great Isambard Kingdom Brunel, had earlier proposed r.b. for the strengthening of a tall chimney but instead used it first in 1825 for the construction of the circular caissons at the ends of the Wapping to Rotherhithe tunnel — still in use today — under the Thames. A form of pozzolanic material — possibly Roman cement — must have been used for these structures because pure lime mortar would have been inadequate in many respects. For example, it would not have bonded to the 228 mm wide by 12 mm thick hoop iron used at intervals in the horizontal joints. Portland cement had just been patented (1824) but would not have been available. These caissons had a diameter of 15.25 m, a wall thickness of 762 mm, and were 21.3 and 12.8 m high. As they sank, their integrity was maintained by 48 wrought-iron bolts of 25 mm diameter built vertically into the brickwork and through timber curbs at the top and bottom of the walling. Tightening of the bolts gave the brickwork walls the necessary shear strength to resist forces from the unequal settlements which occurred as the earth was removed.

It is tempting, but probably erroneous, to regard these early works as the first use of prestressed masonry. According to Beamish,[1.2] Brunel was sufficiently impressed with the performance of the r.b. caissons to experiment further and in 1836 he built the 'Nine Elms' beam, an inverted 'T' spanning 6.5 m (Fig. 1.1) which for 2 years supported a superimposed distributed load of 105.9 kN until it finally broke, under a total load of 303.7 kN, by tensile failure of the hoop-iron reinforcement.

Fig. 1.1 Brunel's
'Nine Elms' beam
(outline according
to Filippi[1.1])

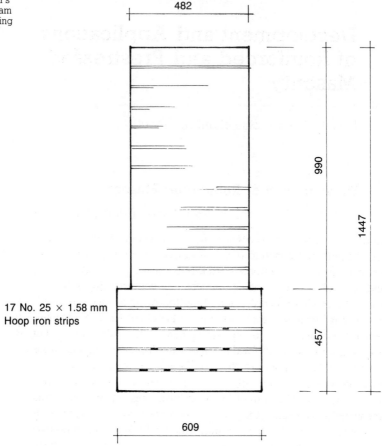

17 No. 25 × 1.58 mm
Hoop iron strips

Initially his contemporaries did not accept that the hoop iron acted in tension, maintaining instead that the resistance was due to the tensile bond (adhesion) of Roman cement mortar to the bricks. This argument was resolved in 1837 by one Colonel Pasley who built three r.b.m. beams each about 450 mm wide by 300 mm deep spanning 3.05 m. One (A) was built in pure cement without reinforcement, the second (B) in pure cement with reinforcement (five strips of hoop iron distributed vertically throughout the section) and the third (C) with the same reinforcement but with bricks laid in 1:3 lime:sand mortar. Beams A and C failed under a load of about 2.2 kN, whereas beam B sustained a load of almost 21 kN. Clearly, only the lower strips acted in tension and when beam B was loaded to failure they snapped. The cross-sectional area of reinforcement was 100.8 mm², or about 0.072 per cent. Brunel senior repeated his 'Nine Elms' beam test during the 1851 Exposition, using the new Portland cement in place of the pozzolanic material used for the 1836 test. This time the maximum imposed load was just over 50 per cent greater, the increase being due to the enhanced adhesion between brick and mortar.

Thereafter, interest in the UK in r.b.m. lapsed for a long period but it was used elsewhere, although not on any great scale. One of the earliest examples was a circular reservoir with walls 762 mm thick reinforced horizontally with hoop iron, built in Georgetown, near Washington, DC, which lasted until 1932.

Systems of reinforcing concrete were being developed and patented towards the end of the nineteenth century, one of which was that by Cottancin in 1889. Edgell[1.3] reports that Cottancin used a fine woven mesh of 4−5 mm diameter steel reinforcement because he believed that the bond between steel and concrete would not be permanent and therefore that the thickness of concrete should be kept to a minimum (not more than 60 mm) and the spacing of steel small to avoid any spalling. Such thin sections required stiffening by ribs which were similarly full of thin bar mesh. Bernstein[1.4] states that it was probably the architect Anatole de Baudot, with whom Cottancin worked on several buildings, who introduced the ribs into the Cottancin floor systems but this seems doubtful. What is more likely is that together they extended it to brickwork, perhaps the finest example of that development being the Church of St Jean de Montmartre (1894−1905), Paris, which is remarkable for the slenderness of its walls and columns. Edgell,[1.3] quoting Marsh,[1.5] describes the construction in some detail. The columns of the c. 13 m wide nave are 440 mm square, rise 10 m from the crypt floor to the nave floor, with arch ribs springing from them to give the floor support, then rise a further 25 m to the roof, with ribs again springing at different heights to support the domed interior. The external walls are only 110 mm thick. According to Filippi,[1.1] the most slender is 35 m high and 9 m wide without intermediate support but, according to Edgell, they have lateral support from gallery floors.

The latter is the case in another and equally remarkable building, Sidwell Street Methodist Church in Exeter, built about 1909. Investigation of the state of the reinforcement by Dr Edgell and the author in 1984 showed very little signs of rust. The maze of thin steel bars in the brickwork (Fig. 1.2) must have made its construction process very difficult. Bernstein[1.4] illustrates this complexity which was doubtless the principal cause of the demise of the system and possibly also of Cottancin's eventual bankruptcy when acting as contractor as well as engineer at Sidwell Street.

The Expanded Metal Company experimented as early at 1912 to determine the increase in resistance to load of brickwork reinforced in

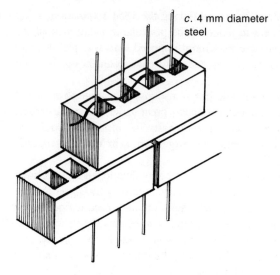

Fig. 1.2 Cottancin's method of reinforcing brickwork

c. 4 mm diameter steel

bed joints. Figures 1.3 and 1.4 illustrate two of these tests, one on a wall beam and the other on a laterally loaded panel. The reinforcement used is still available today for that purpose, as are at least three other proprietary products.

Contemporaneous with St Jean de Montmartre was the construction of four 30 m high and 9.4 m diameter grain storage bins at Louisville, Kentucky. As early as 1913 Filippi built and tested an r.b. beam 203 mm wide and 335 mm deep spanning *c.* clear 3.6 m. It was reinforced horizontally with five 12.7 mm square deformed bars and was possibly the first to use bars instead of hoop iron.

Fig. 1.3 Beam test by Expanded Metal Company, 1912

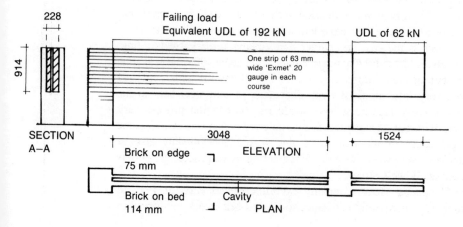

228

914

Failing load
Equivalent UDL of 192 kN

UDL of 62 kN

One strip of 63 mm wide 'Exmet' 20 gauge in each course

SECTION
A–A

3048

1524

Brick on edge
75 mm

ELEVATION

Brick on bed
114 mm

Cavity

PLAN

In India at about this time r.b. was used for small elements such as lintels over doorways. According to Brebner,[1.6] the executive engineer of the local government of Patna suggested that it should also be used for floors and roofs of new buildings because of the steep rise in costs of cement. This led to the first ever substantial programme of research in r.b.m., the results of which were reported comprehensively in 1923.

This work was extensive, to say the least. Its principal aims were three, namely:

(a) to find the most suitable and practicable materials and methods of construction for a range of building elements — walls, beams and slabs — subjected to normal loads and supporting conditions;
(b) to ascertain values for safe adhesion of mortar to brick and steel and the strengths in bending shear and compresson of the composite;
(c) to see whether a theory for r.b. similar to that for r.c. could result in safe design rules.

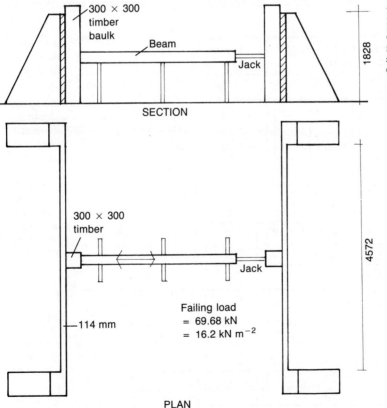

Fig. 1.4 Lateral load test by Expanded Metal Company (from information supplied by the company)

Various other practical aspects, e.g. effect of bond arrangement of bricks, were also examined. In all 282 experiments were conducted, ranging from compressive tensile and shear tests on bricks and mortar to the construction and testing of an earthquake-proof room.

The bricks used were solid, measured 254 × 127 × 76 mm and were combined in different ways to make up slab thicknesses of 76–254 mm (Fig. 1.5). As mentioned above, Brebner was particularly interested in the performance of r.b. slabs so his many experiments encompassed load tests on one- and two-way slabs with spans up to 6.1 m. In these, mild steel bars were placed in joints between the lowest layer of bricks. Where possible, continuous vertical joints through two layers of bricks were avoided and if possible stretching bond was preferred in each course. This could not always be achieved, especially in two-way spans where bricks in the lowest layer had perforce to be laid in 'stack' bond so that bars could be placed in both directions near the bottom to achieve the greatest lever arm.

Brebner used a layer of lime concrete to protect the r.b.m. roof slabs on his many buildings but makes no reference to any waterproofing membrane such as bitumen. In consequence many have not survived the

Fig. 1.5 Examples of reinforced brick masonry slabs tested by Brebner

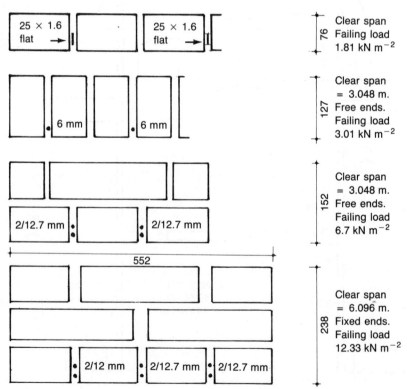

years, although some quite ambitious r.b. cotton mill structures are still in use and it is common even today for r.b. slabs to be used for roof slabs for houses in some parts of India. By 1923 Brebner claimed that more than 277 777 m^2 of slabs had been built in r.b.m.

Brebner tested lintels, beams, including T-beams, wall beams (which he called hanging walls) and columns, heavily reinforced slabs suitable for bridge decking, brick columns with and without reinforcement and even a spiral staircase. Perhaps his most impressive experiment was a 12.19 m span bridge beam, somewhat similar in section to Brunel's 'Nine Elms' beam but on a bigger scale. This was designed to sustain a distributed live load of 380 kN but failed at a load of 1400 kN.

The publication of Brebner's work reawakened interest in the USA and as a result between 1926 and 1932 there were many small series of tests on beams and slabs at more than a dozen universities or technical centres[1.7–1.9] and by Parsons, Stang and McBurney[1.10] at the Bureau of Standards in Washington.

These stimulated a further comprehensive study, even more extensive than Brebner's, conducted over a period of 3 years (1932–34) by the Brick Manufacturers' Association of America, later the Structural Clay Products Research Foundation.[1.11]

Bricks used in this series were considerably stronger than those which Brebner had available. A good first-class brick at Patna where much work was done had an average crushing strength on bed of about 9.5 N mm^{-2}, whereas in the USA in 1932 more than 75 per cent of bricks had a corresponding strength of 20.7 N mm^{-2}. It was realized by Brebner as well as later researchers that the strength on bed ('flatwise' in the USA) is generally greater than on end or on edge and that design must take account of this. This was and is particularly important when perforated bricks are used. On the other hand, perforation aids resistance to shearing stresses between bricks and enhances adhesion by increasing the area of contact between mortar and brick. Both Brebner and Filippi noted that bricks with relatively smooth surfaces gave lower resistance in bending.

In the UK interest was revived in 1937 by Burridge[1.12] who reviewed the history of r.b.m., discussed its potential and suggested design values. About the same time the London Brick Company (LBC) became very interested in it and employed Filippi to design their stand for the 1936 Building Exhibition. Thereafter, they produced a series (unpublished) of data and details on r.b.m. slabs, beams, walls and columns. Hamman and Burridge[1.13] reviewed the history of r.b.m. again but more deeply in April 1939 and reported the results of pilot tests on beams made of two types of brick representing the extremes of the range of strength and water absorption found in bricks generally available at that time. This paper was followed in the same year by Thomas and Simms[1.14] reporting tests on r.b.m. by the Building Research Station. Both papers drew particular attention to the importance of shear as opposed to compressive resistance in bending. Failure in bending compression would be unlikely in r.b.m., the primary criterion being that of shear resistance.

Review of Research in Reinforced Concrete Masonry

Reinforced concrete masonry (r.c.m.) is usually of concrete blocks containing two large voids symmetrically disposed around the centre so that when laid in stretching bond continuous vertical spaces are created for concrete or grout and steel. According to Roberts et al.[1.15] the earliest hollow concrete blocks were made in the UK in about 1850 but the use of r.c.m. as we know it today was not developed until many decades later and — as in r.b.m. — began in seismic areas. Resistance to earthquakes was the primary stimulant so it was in New Zealand and the USA where the early research took place.

Early in this context means about 1930, much later than in r.b.m. Holmes[1.16] describes the history of earthquake shocks over the period of organized European settlement in New Zealand, i.e. from about 1827. During those in 1929 at Murchison and in 1931 at Napier — particularly the latter — there was loss of life from building collapse and falling masonry on a scale which demanded new design rules and building by-laws, and the result was the appearance in 1935 of the New Standard Model Building By-law in which national design for earthquakes was introduced for the first time. This led to the New Zealand Standard Specification 1900 in which the use of unreinforced masonry was restricted to a greater or lesser extent according to the seismic zone in which it was built. In the worst areas it was not permitted at all.

These restrictions led initially to insistence on framing in steel or reinforced concrete for all but the smallest — two or three storey — walling, but in 1959 masonry construction was again allowed provided that it was reinforced. Scrivener,[1.17] in a paper describing research and construction development in New Zealand, attributes 'this resurgence of faith in masonry' to Holmes.

The first tests on reinforced concrete block walls in New Zealand took place in 1965.[1.18] They were racking load tests on square shear walls, either unreinforced or with reinforced vertical edges. Failure was by yielding of the steel. Shear failures were induced in a second series of tests by vertically loading the top corner where the lateral load was applied. In the USA, Converse[1.19] had earlier (1946) achieved the same effect by applying load diagonally and Schneider[1.20] in 1959 forced shear failure by heavy vertical edge steel.

These tests, all static and monotonic, were followed by Scrivener and

Williams[1.21] with static cyclic load tests in which aspect ratio, bearing load and amount and disposition of steel were varied. High aspect ratio, low bearing load and a low amount of edge steel resulted in ductile failure. Conversely, square walls (aspect ratio 1) with high restraining load and a greater amount of vertical steel gave diagonal tension failure. It was found that as well as diagonal tension cracks shear walls at failure exhibited splitting of masonry at the toe due to high compression. This became much worse under dynamic cycling and led to a development by Priestley and Bridgeman[1.22] of confining plates which successfully reduced the lateral spread of the mortar and also laterally restrained the vertical steel.

In these tests horizontal steel was found to be better than vertical steel in controlling the diagonal cracking because it was better able to resist the tendency of the top part of the wall to move in relation to the bottom. Thus means of incorporating horizontal steel in grooves along tops of cross webs of blocks in addition to vertical steel in cells were advantageous. Such units in concrete are readily available.

Research into structural uses of r.c.m. in the UK has not had the stimulus of the need to consider seismicity nor until fairly recently has there been much demand for masonry for retaining walls, for example, or for other uses demanding knowledge of performance in bending. Hence reliable design information has been lacking, but no longer. Roberts[1.23] reported on r.c.m. subject to lateral loading in 1975 and 1976. This information was included later in a paper by Cranston and Roberts[1.24] and summarized with additional material by Roberts[1.25] in 1979.

Research in North America has been much more extensive. There are many papers, too numerous to identify individually here, in the proceedings of the frequent conferences which have been held there in recent years which have examined a wide range of aspects of r.c.m.[1.26−1.29]

Research goes on apace in r.b.m. and r.c.m. world-wide and augurs well for the future of reinforced masonry, but this short review should not end without reference to the problems of dimensional stability inherent in all uses of masonry, reinforced or not, namely the effects of temperature and moisture change, and long- and short-term loading. The state of the art in respect of these has been comprehensively reviewed recently by Jessop.[1.30] Aspects of durability are equally important, in particular the risk of corrosion of reinforcement. In the UK the relatively high incidence of corrosion of wall ties has led to increased weights of protective coatings, more widespread use of rust-resisting steels and thickness of cover being related to degree of exposure. These requirements are incorporated in BS 5628:Part 2:1985 *Use of Masonry. Structural Use of Reinforced and Prestressed Masonry.*

Applications of Reinforced Masonry

In the UK r.b.m. has not yet been used to any great extent but use and interest are growing. For the most part work has been confined to walling, particularly retaining walls (Fig. 1.6); r.b.m. slabs and beams have been used in very special buildings such as the office building (Fig. 1.7) for

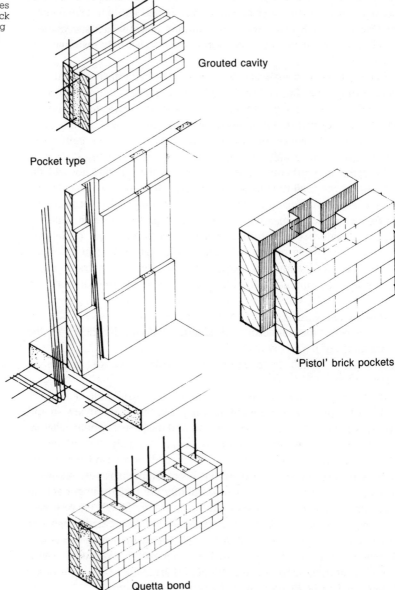

Fig. 1.6 Examples of reinforced brick masonry retaining wall construction

Grouted cavity

Pocket type

'Pistol' brick pockets

Quetta bond

a brick company described by Bradshaw and Drinkwater,[1.31] but at present seem unlikely to play any major role in horizontal structures in which concrete has long predominated. Even the use of hollow clay blocks in floors has now vanished from the UK despite its wide use in Italy, particularly, and elsewhere in Europe.

Early examples of use (before the Second World War) are mentioned by Hamman and Burridge,[1.13] one of which is a canopy on the LBC 1936 exhibition stand, and another is the strengthening to resist lateral loading of half-brick spandrel walls cladding an ICI laboratory building in Manchester. These are small beer compared to Brebner's work.

Fig. 1.7 Reinforced brick masonry beam and slab, Head Office Armitage Brick Ltd. J Brunton and Partners, architects; Bradshaw Buckton and Tonge, consulting engineers

Interest lapsed during and after the Second World War but was revived between 1960 and 1970 with various publications produced by the industry. Sutherland[1.32] reviewed the scope and potential of r.b.m., drawing particular attention to *in situ* and prefabricated r.b.m. pocket-type retaining walls and illustrating examples. Maurenbrecher[1.33] designed one of the earliest of these in the UK (Fig. 1.8).

Reinforced masonry has been used to a small extent in agricultural buildings. Dinnie and Beard[1.34] describe designs for circular and rectangular r.b.m. silos. Drinkwater and Bradshaw[1.35] give examples of retaining walls for slurry tanks and grain stores in r.b.m. Adams and Saul[1.36] describe r.c.m. walls for retaining silage, piers for strengthening gables and an r.c.m. diaphragm gantry crane wall.

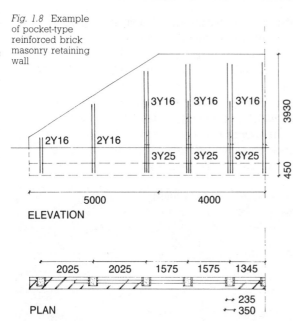

Fig. 1.8 Example of pocket-type reinforced brick masonry retaining wall

ELEVATION

PLAN

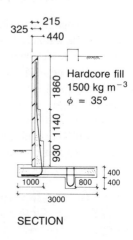

SECTION

Fig. 1.9 Reinforced brick masonry water tank for Armitage Brick Company Ltd. G D Johnson, consulting engineer

Sharp[1.37] pioneered the use of concrete blockwork in diaphragm walls at a time of shortage of structural steel.

Johnson[1.38] designed a large r.b.m. circular water tank (Fig. 1.9) having a capacity of 541 m³. It is 10.5 m in diameter and 8.25 m high with a 6.25 m height of water. The design of this impressive structure,

which is partly buried on one side, was based on the design of r.c. tanks. Bradshaw[1.39] used r.b.m. for certain elements of the predominantly unreinforced structure of a new Methodist church in Leeds, illustrating the flexibility of this form of construction, i.e. adding tensile resistance only where necessary and thus keeping costs low. Perhaps the most recent example of the use of r.b.m., again in a predominantly load-bearing building is another office for a brick company, also designed by Bradshaw, Thompson and Bell.[1.40]

It is to the USA that one must turn for the most stimulating examples of the use of r.m., whether of r.b.m. or r.c.m. Hanson[1.41] and Sallada and Wakefield[1.42] describe respectively 17- and 20-storey apartment towers in Denver which they designed using grouted cavity masonry shear walls reinforced to resist seismic forces. Wide twin tee prefabricated prestressed r.c. slabs (Fig. 1.10) span 9 m or more on to these walls to which they are tied with steel embedded in *in situ* screeds. These act structurally to bind the slabs together to form horizontal diaphragms (Fig. 1.11). At the time they were built these impressive buildings were almost certainly the highest in this type of shear wall structure but it is equally likely that they will have been surpassed in that respect in the two decades since then. However, nothing could demonstrate more effectively than they the suitability of masonry for shear wall structures of appropriate plan layout. In both instances saving of cost over framed construction was given as the principal reason for the choice of r.m.

In the 20-storey examples it was found necessary to resort to

Fig. 1.10 Construction of Park Mayfair East. Engineers: Sallada and Hanson, Denver

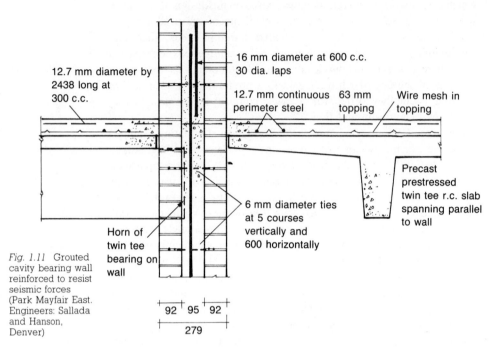

12.7 mm diameter by 2438 long at 300 c.c.

16 mm diameter at 600 c.c. 30 dia. laps

12.7 mm continuous perimeter steel

63 mm topping

Wire mesh in topping

Precast prestressed twin tee r.c. slab spanning parallel to wall

6 mm diameter ties at 5 courses vertically and 600 horizontally

Horn of twin tee bearing on wall

92 ' 95 ' 92

279

Fig. 1.11 Grouted cavity bearing wall reinforced to resist seismic forces (Park Mayfair East. Engineers: Sallada and Hanson, Denver)

combinations of brick and block to achieve the cost target. Allowable stresses were then limited by the strength of the weaker material. The rheological behaviour of composite reinforced walls such as these would be of great interest but as far as is known this has not yet been reported.

Sutherland[1.43] reported in 1970 on tall buildings solely of concrete blockwork.

Development of Prestressed Masonry: Research and Applications

Apart from M. I. Brunel's use of wrought-iron rods for the caissons of the Thames Tunnel, which might or might not be regarded as the first use of prestressed brick masonry (p.b.m.), depending on one's point of view, effective development had to wait until the establishment of prestressed concrete. The first use of p.b.m. known to the writer, believed to be the first ever use, is that by Felix J. Samuely in 1953 for stiffening piers for the tall side walls of a school assembly hall[1.44] at a time when steel was in short supply.

In 1961 Tasker studied the performance of experimental prestressed brickwork walls for use on reactive soils and concluded that economical design could result.[1.45]

In 1963 r.b.m. was used for the tall (7 m high) walls cladding a steel-framed factory in the north of England.[1.46] The engineer quoted the work of Poljakov[1.47] on creep in ordinary and reinforced masonry as providing essential data which encouraged the use of r.b.m. for the project. The work by Lenczner[1.48] on this vital subject came later.

The prestressing of ceramic tiles to form 'planks' for the support of larger ceramic flooring units — the Stahlton system — was a development about this time. Thomas[1.49] reported in 1969 tests of p.b.m. beams by himself and Plowman. Similar experiments were carried out by Mehta and Finchner[1.50] in Texas at that time.

Circumferential and vertical prestressing (Fig. 1.12) was used by Foster[1.51] for the clay brickwork walls of a 12 m diameter and 4.9 m deep water tank in 1967, following the design of similar structures in concrete.

Curtin, Adams and Sloan post-tensioned the p.b.m. spandrel walls of

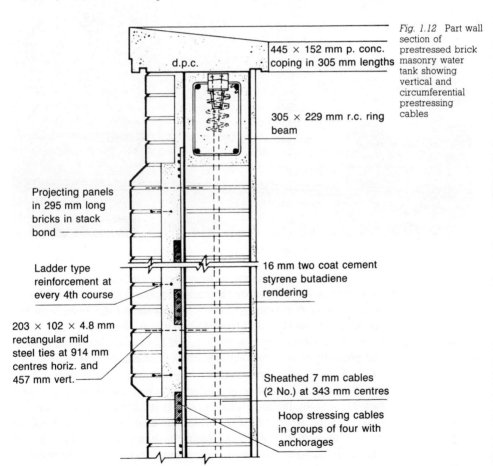

Fig. 1.12 Part wall section of prestressed brick masonry water tank showing vertical and circumferential prestressing cables

d.p.c.

445 × 152 mm p. conc. coping in 305 mm lengths

305 × 229 mm r.c. ring beam

Projecting panels in 295 mm long bricks in stack bond

Ladder type reinforcement at every 4th course

203 × 102 × 4.8 mm rectangular mild steel ties at 914 mm centres horiz. and 457 mm vert.

16 mm two coat cement styrene butadiene rendering

Sheathed 7 mm cables (2 No.) at 343 mm centres

Hoop stressing cables in groups of four with anchorages

Fig. 1.13
Prestressed
brickwork wall,
Orsborn Memorial
Halls, Boscombe.
Curtins Consulting
Engineers. Photo:
Frank Walter
Designs

school buildings to enable them to be positioned on the edge of cantilevered floors forward of columns yet able to resist the wind forces from continuous glazing above.[1.52] More recently the same team has researched and applied post-tensioning to p.b.m. diaphragm walls, vastly improving their resistance in bending, and by example leading to a recent and possibly far-reaching application in civil engineering, namely the brickwork bridge abutments for the Glinton bypass near Peterborough.[1.53] Another and very attractive use of post-tensioned masonry also by the same designers[1.54] is the external p.b.m. walling of a Salvation Army hall (Fig. 1.13), and a further recent example is its use at a fire station in Rushden, Northants.[1.55] Phipps and Montague[1.56] have examined the use in the UK of prestressing to enhance the performance of concrete block masonry diaphragm walls, and in New Zealand prestressing has been applied to external blockwork walls by incorporating sheathed cables in a wall cavity or in the usual hollows in the blocks themselves.[1.57]

Other work in this field forms part of the veritably world-wide explosion of interest and research in structural uses of masonry over the last three decades. Subsequent chapters of this book will be based on this work and will give references as appropriate.

Advantages and Disadvantages of Reinforced and Prestressed Masonry

The principal advantage is clearly and simply the addition of tensile resistance to otherwise brittle materials such as concrete, fired clay or calcium silicate masonry. Their other attributes — assuming sound manufacture of their components — of good appearance, durability, low maintenance, good fire resistance and sound insulation, freedom from infestation and flexibility give them almost the best balance of properties. They cannot claim to give good thermal insulation by today's standards against heat loss although in hot countries they give economical resistance to solar gain.

Their principal failing seems to the writer to be their lack of resistance to penetration by driving rain when used without clear cavities at least 50 mm wide. This presents great difficulties when considering their use for grouted cavity or filled cell construction in countries like the UK, or other areas of geographically severe or even moderate exposure, without rendering or other external protection. That being so, the important claim that masonry is unique in being simultaneously structure and finish — at least for grouted r.m. — is insupportable for wide use here with today's standard of workmanship. It may be that techniques used elsewhere to meet this particular problem will have to be adopted. In Canada, Switzerland and South Africa internal renderings of rich cement mortar have been used on the inside faces of solid facing brick walls. In East London a bituminous coat has been applied. Concern about rain penetration has also been expressed by Eppel[1.58] who reported an increase of instances in Canada.

Diaphragm walls are reported to be free from problems of rain penetration. Post-tensioned diaphragms are demonstrations of how masonry can be turned into virtually a new structural material suitable for a wide range of buildings as well as for retaining walls and bridge abutments. A particular advantage of masonry structures is that shuttering is either not required or needed in only minimal quantities, as in pocket-type retaining walls.

The greater part of masonry structure built to date has been cellular building, such as apartments or hostels, in which there is repetition of plan arrangement on successive floors so that loads are, sensibly, taken directly to foundations. This is true for both reinforced and unreinforced walls. Where it is necessary to break this vertical continuity, such as lower floors in hotels, it has been necessary to revert to steel or r.c. structure. Experiments have been undertaken to test the performance of

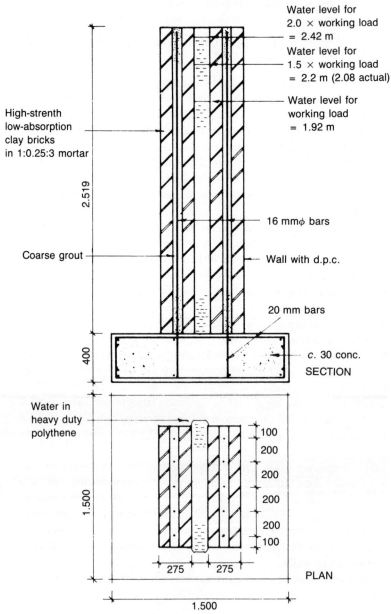

Fig. 1.14 Test walls and loading arrangement for creep test on reinforced brickwork masonry retaining walls

Water level for
2.0 × working load
= 2.42 m

Water level for
1.5 × working load
= 2.2 m (2.08 actual)

Water level for
working load
= 1.92 m

High-strenth
low-absorption
clay bricks
in 1:0.25:3 mortar

2.519

16 mmϕ bars

Coarse grout

Wall with d.p.c.

20 mm bars

c. 30 conc.
SECTION

400

Water in
heavy duty
polythene

100
200
200
200
200
100

1.500

275   275

PLAN

1.500

r.b.m. box beam structures, in which masonry forms the webs and r.c. floors the flanges. These have been reported by Plowman, Sutherland and Couzens[1.59] but have never been used in practice. Tests were done with both reinforced and prestressed walls, the latter being much the more successful. Gero[1.60] reported model studies of a prestressed masonry space structure with these practical uses in mind.

In the design of prestressed walls it is of course necessary to take careful account of creep, as has been mentioned briefly above. In this respect it has been shown that concrete block masonry creeps considerably more than fired clay masonry. It also shrinks (whereas clay expands) so losses in prestress are much higher. Sinha[1.61] subjected r.b.m. retaining walls to sustained loading to determine creep in bending (Fig. 1.14).

Concrete blocks, being much easier and quicker to lay than bricks, give more economical walls which are also easier to reinforce. There has also been a considerable advance in the quality and variety of facings that are now available so blocks are greatly favoured in some countries. However, the range of finishes in countries rich in brick clays like the UK is much wider.

Fig. 1.15 Interior of church at Atlantida, Uruguay

Fig. 1.16 Church
of St Mary, Deare,
Alberta. Architect:
Douglas J Cardinal

Whether of clay or concrete or calcium silicate, one other obvious,
though not the most economical, advantage of unit masonry (particularly
of brick format) construction is the ease with which curved walls can
be built without expensive shuttering. A church at Atlantida, Uruguay,
is one remarkable example (Fig. 1.15). Another, even more spectacular,
is the church of St Mary, at Deare, Alberta (Figs 1.16 and 1.17). The
'cavity' walling of this consists of two one-brick (200 mm) thick leaves
enclosing a 200 mm thick core of reinforced concrete. A somewhat
arbitrary definition of grouted cavity r.b.m. restricts the thickness of
the core to 100 mm, beyond which it is classed as cased concrete. Under
that definition St Mary, Deare, is not r.b.m. but no other building shows
better what r.b.m. can achieve in curved walling.

Rectilinear design has had a powerful hold on designers even from
antiquity. Industrialization increased this with continuous processes for
boards, sheets and the like. The advent of framed construction added
to it and the current almost innate need to think in frames leads directly
to rectilinear grids on the drawing board. Rectangular spaces and volumes
follow. Small unit masonry construction, reinforced or prestressed where
appropriate, offers an economical way out of this impasse.

References

1.1   Filippi H 1933 *Brick Engineering — Reinforced Brick Masonry, Principles
of Design and Construction* vol 3, Brick Manufacturers Association of
America

Fig. 1.17 Church
of St Mary, Deare,
Alberta. Architect:
Douglas J Cardinal

1.2 Beamish R 1862 *Memoirs of the Life of Sir Marc Isambard Brunel* Longman, Green, Longman and Roberts

1.3 Edgell G J 1985 The remarkable structures of Paul Cottancin. *Structural Engineer* **63A** (7) 201−7

1.4 Bernstein D 1979 Some early reinforced brickwork masterpieces revisited. *Proceedings of the Fifth International Brick Masonry Conference* Washington, DC Brick Institute of America

1.5 Marsh C M 1904 *Reinforced Concrete* Constable, London

1.6 Brebner A 1923 *Notes on Reinforced Brickwork. Tests, Theory and Actual Construction of Reinforced Brickwork in India* Govt of India Public Works Dept Technical Paper No 38 (2 vols), Govt Printing Office, India

1.7 Whittemore J W, Dear P S 1933 *A Comparison of the Performance Characteristics of Reinforced Brick Masonry Slabs* Virginia Polytechnic Institute Engineering Experimental Station Bulletin 15

1.8 Withey M O 1933 Tests of brick masonry beams. *ASTM Proceedings* **33** Part II

1.9 Lent L B 1931 Reinforced brick masonry. *Journal of the American Ceramic Society* **14**

1.10 Parsons D E, Stang A H, McBurney J W 1932 Shear tests of reinforced brick masonry beams. *National Bureau of Standards RP504, Journal of Research* **9**: 749−68

1.11 American Ceramic Society 1933 *Reports of Committee on Reinforced Brick Masonry of the National Brick Manufactuers' Research Foundation* American Ceramic Society Bulletins 1−8

1.12 Burridge L W 1937 Survey of principles, development and potentialities of R.B. reinforced brickwork. *RIBA Journal* **44**(6): 285−95

1.13 Hamman C W, Burridge L W 1939 Reinforced brickwork. *Structural*

Engineer **17**(4)

1.14   Thomas F G, Simms L G 1939 The strength of some reinforced brickwork beams in bending and in shear. *Structural Engineer* **17**(7)

1.15   Roberts J J, Tovey A K, Cranston W B, Beeby A W 1983 *Concrete Masonry Designers Handbook* Eyre and Spottiswoode, Leatherhead

1.16   Holmes I L 1969 Masonry building in high intensity seismic zones. In Johnson F B (ed) *Designing, Engineering and Constructing in Masonry Products* Gulf Publishing Company, Houston, Texas pp 348–56

1.17   Scrivener J C 1976 Reinforced masonry in a seismic area — research and construction development in New Zealand. *Proceedings of the First Canadian Masonry Symposium* Calgary 1976 pp 371–82

1.18   Scrivener J C 1966 Concrete masonry wall panel tests — static racking tests with predominant flexural effect. *New Zealand Concrete Construction* July pp 119–25

1.19   Converse F J 1946 Tests on reinforced concrete masonry. *Building Standards Monthly* Feb: 4–13

1.20   Schneider R R 1959 *Lateral Load Tests on Reinforced Grouted Masonry Shear Walls* Engineering Centre, University of Southern California. State of California, Dept of Public Works, Division of Architecture, Sacramento, California

1.21   Scrivener J C, Williams D 1971 Behavior of reinforced masonry shear walls under cyclic loading. *Bulletin of the New Zealand Society for Earthquake Engineering* **4**(2) April

1.22   Priestley M N, Bridgeman D O 1974 Seismic resistance of masonry shear walls. *Bulletin of the New Zealand Society for Earthquake Engineering* **7**(4)

1.23   Roberts J J 1976 The behaviour of vertically reinforced concrete blockwork subject to lateral loads. *Proceedings of the First Canadian Masonry Conference* Calgary 1976 pp 257–74

1.24   Cranston W B, Roberts J J 1976 The structural behaviour of concrete masonry walls — reinforced and unreinforced. *Structural Engineer* **54**(11) Nov

1.25   Roberts J J 1979 Recent research on reinforced concrete blockwork. *Proceedings of the Symposium — Reinforced and Prestressed Masonry* London 1979, Cement and Concrete Association, Wexham Springs

1.26   *Proceedings of the First Canadian Masonry Symposium* Calgary 1976

1.27   *Proceedings of the Second Canadian Masonry Symposium* Ottawa 1980

1.28   *Proceedings of the North American Masonry Conference* Boulder Colorado 1978

1.29   *Proceedings of the Third Canadian Masonry Symposium* Edmonton 1983

1.30   Jessop E 1980 Moisture, thermal, elastic and creep properties of masonry: a state of the art report. *Proceedings of the Second Canadian Masonry Symposium* Ottawa 1980 pp 505–20

1.31   Bradshaw R E, Drinkwater J P 1983 Reinforced brickwork in the George Armitage office block, Robin Hood, Wakefield. *Structural Engineer 61A*(8) Aug

1.32   Sutherland R J M 1981 Brick and block masonry in engineering. *Proceedings of the Institution of Civil Engineers* Part 1 **70** Feb: 31–63

1.33   Maurenbrecher A H P 1977 In Foster D (ed) *Reinforced Brickwork: Pocket Type Retaining Wall* SCP 13, Old Weston, Huntingdon, Cambs

1.34 Dinnie A, Beard R 1970 Reinforced brickwork silos for grain storage. *Proceedings of the British Ceramic Society* Loadbearing Brickwork (3), **17** Feb: 127–35

1.35 Drinkwater J P, Bradshaw R E 1982 Reinforced and prestressed masonry in agriculture. *Proceedings of Conference, Institutions of Civil and Structural Engineers* Thomas Telford Ltd, London

1.36 Adams S, Saul J E 1982 Examples of the use of reinforced blockwork. *Proceedings of Conference Institutions of Civil and Structural Engineers* Thomas Telford Ltd, London

1.37 Sharp W 1986 Paper 6. *Proceedings of the Symposium 'Practical Design of Masonry'* Institution of Civil Engineers, London

1.38 Johnson G D 1980 Design and construction of a reinforced brickwork tank. *Proceedings of the Second Canadian Masonry Symposium* Ottawa

1.39 Bradshaw R E 1982 Reinforced brickwork in the Hyde Park Methodist Church, Leeds. *Proceedings of Conference Institutions of Civil and Structural Engineers* 1982, Thomas Telford Ltd, London

1.40 Bradshaw R E, Thompson D, Bell S E New head office for Accrington Brick and Tile Co. Ltd. *Structural Engineer* **67**(16) Aug

1.41 Hanson G C 1969 Park Mayfair East. In Johnson F B (ed) *Designing, Engineering and Constructing with Masonry Products* Gulf Publishing Company, Houston, Texas p 400

1.42 Sallada J W, Wakefield D A 1970 Park Lane Towers Complex, Denver, Colorado. In West H W H, Speed K H (eds) *Proceedings of the Second International Brick Masonry Conference* Stoke-on-Trent

1.43 Sutherland R J M 1969 *High-rise Concrete Blockwork* Technical Papoer PCS 37, Concrete Society, London

1.44 Samuely F J 1953 Note on design of assembly hall walls. Blackwell Secondary Modern School. Assembly, gymnasia etc. *RIBA Journal* Oct

1.45 Tasker H E 1964 *Recommendations for the Use of Prestressed Brick or Block Walls on Reactive Soils* Technical Record 52:75:349, Dept of Works, Commonwealth Experimental Building Station

1.46 Neill J A 1966 *Post-tensioned Brickwork and its Use in the Construction of a Factory at Darlington* Technical Note 1, 9 May 1966, Clay Products Technical Bureau (now Brick Development Association, Winkfield, Windsor, Berks)

1.47 Poljakov S V 1962 *Some Problems of Creep in Ordinary and Reinforced Masonry Members* International Council for Building Research Studies and Documentation, Paris

1.48 Lenczner D 1980 Design of brick masonry for elastic and creep movements. *Proceedings of the Second Canadian Masonry Symposium* Ottawa

1.49 Thomas K 1969 Current post tensioned and prestressed brickwork and ceramics in Great Britain. In Johnson F B (ed) *Designing, Engineering and Constructing with Masonry Products* Gulf Publishing Company, Houston, Texas p 285

1.50 Mehta K C, Finchner D 1970 Structural behaviour of pretensioned prestressed masonry beams. In West H W H, Speed K H (eds) *Proceedings of the Second International Brick Masonry Conference* Stoke-on-Trent April 1970

1.51   Foster D 1970 Design and construction of a prestressed brickwork water tank. In West H W H, Speed K H (eds) *Proceedings of the Second International Brick Masonry Conference* Stoke-on-Trent April 1970 pp 287–94

1.52   Curtin W G, Adams R S, Sloan M 1975 The use of post tensioned brickwork in the SCD system. *Proceedings of the British Ceramic Society* **24**: 235–45

1.53   BDA 1989 Post tensioned bridge abutments. *The Brick Bulletin* Spring, Brick Development Association, Winkfield, Windsor, Berks

1.54   Shaw G, Othick G J, and Priestley C L 1986 *The Orsborn Memorial Halls at Boscombe* Engineers File Note No 6, Brick Development Association, Winkfield, Windsor, Berks

1.55   Allen L N 1986 *Post-tensioned Brickwork at Rushden Fire Station* Engineers File Note No 1, Brick Development Association, Winkfield, Windsor, Berks

1.56   Phipps M E, Montague T I 1987 The testing of plain and prestressed concrete blockwork beams and walls of geometric cross section. *Masonry International* **1**(3): 71–108

1.57   *Concrete* **4**(9) Sept 1970

1.58   Eppel F J 1980 State of the art report: rain penetration of masonry. *Proceedings of the Second Canadian Masonry Symposium* Ottawa 1980 pp 521–36

1.59   Plowman J M, Sutherland R J M, Couzens M R 1967 The testing of reinforced brickwork and concrete slabs forming box beams. *Structural Engineer* **45**(11) Nov

1.60   Gero J S 1969 Prestressed masonry — reinforced concrete space structure. In Johnson F B (ed) *Designing, Engineering and Constructing with Masonry Products* Gulf Publishing Company, Houston, Texas

1.61   Sinha B P SCP 14 *Reinforced Brickwork: Retaining Walls Long Term Tests* Vine Cottage, Brington Road, Old Weston, Huntingdon

2 Materials and Material Properties

N G Shrive, Professor of Civil Engineering,
University of Calgary

Introduction

Masonry is a composite of units (bricks, blocks or stone) jointed together
by mortar. In reinforced and prestressed masonry, two more components
are utilized to create the structural element — steel and grout. The latter
may be thought of as a fluid concrete mix with relatively small top-size
aggregate, used to fill cavities in the masonry, typically those with steel
in. The grout thus provides the connection between steel and masonry,
enabling composite action to be developed.

Three factors affect the quality of plain masonry. The quality of the
units, the quality of the mortar and the quality of the workmanship in
putting them together. Typically therefore, emphasis has been placed
in codes and standards on the properties and variability of the component
materials, the view being that good masonry will result from a
combination of good units and consistent, compatible mortar. This view
has been extended to reinforced and prestressed masonry, where again
the components are typically tested in isolation from each other, rather
than in combined form — this time, all four. Workmanship, however,
does affect properties.[2.1, 2.2] Thus in instances where the properties of
masonry as a whole are important, testing of samples of the masonry
may be more appropriate than just testing of the components.

In this chapter, the component materials of masonry and their properties
will be discussed, then the properties of masonry with some final remarks
about reinforcing and prestressing steel and its protection.

Units

Unit Types

Masonry units are typically bricks or blocks. Bricks are normally thought
of as clay bricks and concrete is normally associated with blocks.
However, it is possible to obtain concrete units of the same dimensions
as clay bricks — that is, concrete bricks — and fired clay units of similar

Fig. 2.1 The dimensions and faces of a masonry unit

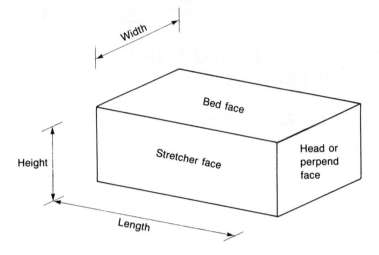

geometry to hollow concrete blocks. Although the material association with the terms brick and block can thus be misleading, it continues. Masonry units, however, are now defined by size. The terms used to define the dimensions of a unit are shown in Fig. 2.1. To be a brick a unit has dimensions:

> Length ≤ 300 mm
> Width ≤ 250 mm
> Height ≤ 120 mm.

Blocks are larger and have dimensions:

> Length 300 ≤ l ≤ 600 mm
> Width   ≤ 300 mm
> Height   ≤ 300 mm.

Units of even larger dimension are 'specials' as are units of special shape for specific purposes.

'Hollow' blocks are commonly used in North America and Australasia in reinforced masonry. Features defined by many of the terms associated with hollow units are depicted in Fig. 2.2. Units, whether brick or block, are 'hollow' if the net cross-sectional area is between 50 and 75 per cent of the gross cross-sectional area. Units are 'solid' if the net cross-sectional area is 75 per cent or greater of the gross. Thus a perforated unit may well be termed 'solid' and treated as such. A common form of construction with hollow units is face-shell bedded masonry, where mortar is placed only on the face-shells when one course of units is bedded on top of another. Face-shell bedded hollow masonry has a few peculiarities of its own.

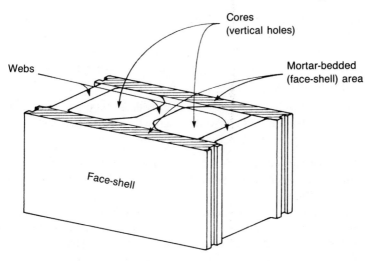

Cores
(vertical holes)

Webs

Mortar-bedded
(face-shell) area

Face-shell

Stone is also used in masonry and may be dressed to a prismatic shape. Stone masonry has been post-tensioned,[2.3, 2.4] but recent emphasis has been on reinforcing or post-tensioning clay and concrete masonry. Stone will not be considered further here.

Clay Units

The properties of clay units depend on the mineralogic composition of the clays used to manufacture the unit, the manufacturing process and the firing temperature.

The mix for producing clay units consists of clays, some silica used partly as a filler, ground particles and dust from old bricks, some feldspar and water. Water is added to make the mix mouldable. Dry pressed bricks are formed from a clay mix of some 10−12 per cent water whereas stiff-plastic pressed bricks begin life a little stickier at 14−17 per cent water content. The most common bricks are extruded initially as columns of 'stiff mud' at some 15−25 per cent water content. The columns of 'mud' extruded from the augur are cut into bricks by wires (like cheese wires).

The moulding process establishes characteristic porosity and planes of weakness in the unit: for example, an extruded unit has to lose more water than a dry pressed unit and may therefore be more porous; and slip planes in the clay during extrusion may become planes for crack extension when masonry is compressed perpendicular to the bedding plane.

After moulding, the units are dried and then fired in a kiln at temperatures between 850 and 1250 °C, with the 1000−1100 °C range being the most common. The firing temperature, the time at that temperature and the size of the particles in the mix all affect the extent of the chemical and thermodynamic reactions which occur in the kiln. There is some vitrification during firing with amorphous alumino-silicates being the major products. Many of these products hydrate later in the presence of moisture, causing clay units to expand with time. Units can be placed in three categories of growth by their expansion over 5 years:

Low   growth ≤ 0.06 per cent (600 $\mu\epsilon$)
Medium 0.06 per cent ≤ growth ≤ 0.12 per cent
High   0.12 per cent ≤ growth

Also, internal stresses caused by phase transformations and other thermal effects are not fully relieved: clay units tend to fail in an almost explosive, brittle fashion.

As there are 1500 or more units on a single kiln car, the units are subject to different temperature/time regimes. Even though there are gaps between the units, those on the outside of the stack on the car are heated up faster, stay at the high temperature longer and are cooled more rapidly than those on the inside of the stack. Thus units from a single clay mix will have different mechanical and physical properties. A certain level of variability is inherent in clay masonry.

Even within a clay unit there will be a variation in properties. The inside takes longer to heat up and cool down than the outside. In order to achieve more even firing through the units, manufacturers create holes (cores) perpendicular to the bed face during extrusion. It is thus not too far from any point inside the unit to a hot surface during firing. 'Frogging' (moulding a triangular groove in the top surface) has two effects, pushing the clay mix well into the corners of the mould, and helping to even the firing of the brick.

Calcium Silicate Units

Calcium silicate bricks are also known as sand−lime bricks. They are produced by pressing a mixture of lime and a fine siliceous sand in a mould and curing by autoclaving. The lime and silica react with water during autoclaving in the pozzolanic reaction (lime plus silica plus water go to calcium silicate hydrate, the same strength-giving product as in hydrated Portland cement). Calcium silicate bricks are thus a more compact and fine-grained version of a concrete brick. In contrast to clay units, calcium silicate units shrink with time, in the order of 0.03 per cent (300 $\mu\epsilon$).

Concrete Units

Concrete units are made from Portland cement concrete, as the name implies. Bricks having a compact, tight-textured appearance can be produced from pressing concrete in a mould. These bricks have similar properties to calcium silicate bricks. More open-textured concrete units are obtained if the concrete is compacted by vibration: most concrete blocks are compacted by vibration, so have the open-textured appearance. The cement and aggregate are weighed and mixed with the minimum water possible to give a 'damp earth' consistency; zero slump, just enough water for hydration. Set volumes of the mix are fed into moulds and vibrated (really vibrated!). Units are then demoulded and usually steam cured at about 80 °C. Normal-weight blocks are produced from normal-weight concrete, lightweight blocks from lightweight aggregate concrete. Aerated blocks have an aerating agent to produce bubbles in the cement paste. These latter sorts of blocks are used structurally, and for their thermal insulation capabilities, but are not typically used in reinforced or prestressed applications.

Concrete units behave similarly to concrete in many ways — their strength increases with time, they creep, they shrink. The range of permanent shrinkage is $0.03-0.05$ per cent ($300-500$ $\mu\epsilon$) for normal and lightweight blocks. Aerated units can shrink by as much as 0.1 per cent.

Sampling and Characteristic Values

Methods of sampling are specified in national codes and standards. Units should be selected at random from batches and pallets, and a minimum number of units is required to provide sufficient knowledge about the variability of the property being measured. If the variability in strength is too high on initial testing for example, further testing may be required[2.5] or a higher penalty paid in determining characteristic strength.[2.6]

Characteristic values of properties are often used in masonry in order to deal with the variability of the material. As more and more measurements are made of a property, so knowledge increases about the average value and how widely distributed the measured values are about that average. In statistical terms, there is more confidence about the mean and variance of the distribution of measured values.

Suppose n samples are tested for a particular property and thus n individual values $x_1, x_2, \ldots x_n$ are obtained (x_i with $i = 1$ to n). The mean value

$$\bar{x} = \frac{1}{n} \sum_{i=1}^{n} x_i$$

(the sum of the n values divided by the number of values, n). The variance of the values indicates how widely distributed the values are about the mean, with the square root of the variance being the standard deviation S of the distribution.

$$S^2 = \frac{1}{n-1} \sum_{i=1}^{n} (x_i - \bar{x})^2.$$

Deducting a number of standard deviations from the mean value establishes a value — a characteristic value — below which only a small number of results may be expected to fall. For example, with a normal distribution, 16 per cent of results may be expected to fall below the mean less one standard deviation, 2.3 per cent below the mean less two standard deviations and only 0.14 per cent below the mean less three standard deviations.

Typically, however, not enough tests are done to establish that the distribution is normal. Thus the number of standard deviations which must be deducted from the mean depends on the number of measurements made (the value of n) and how variable these are (the value of the variance S^2, or $s^2/\bar{x}$, the coefficient of variation).

Strength

The compressive strength of units is determined from 'single unit' tests wherein individual units are compressed between the platens of a testing machine. Most units are squat in shape, so the high unit strengths measured are partly a result of the excessive effect of platen restraint in such tests. In a compression test, the test machine platens do not expand to the lateral Poisson strain of the specimen, but restrain that expansion. The restraint causes a zone of triaxial compression to develop in the specimen near the specimen/platen interface. As compressive test specimens become more squat, this zone becomes a bigger and bigger proportion of the volume of the specimen, and the measured strength becomes a greater multiple of the genuine uniaxial compressive strength. The strengths determined in single unit tests do not reflect directly in masonry strength: 100 N mm^{-2} units do not give 100 N mm^{-2} masonry. This is not because of the platen effect in single unit tests alone, but also because of the effect of the mortar in the masonry, as discussed later. Generally, however, stronger units from a given manufacturing process will give stronger masonry for a given mortar type. Units of similar single unit compressive strength but made by different manufacturing techniques may give different masonry strengths.

Hollow units which are to be face-shell bedded (only have mortar applied along the face-shells (see Fig. 2.2)) should be tested by loading through the face-shells only.

Two flexural strengths can be determined for a masonry unit: the modulus of rupture for out-of-plane bending (the flexural stress varies across the width of the unit), and the transverse strength for in-plane bending (the flexural stress varies along the length of the unit). The unit modulus of rupture affects masonry flexural strength when failure occurs with a crack running through head joints and the units above and below — as can occur in a wall being flexed horizontally (the crack thus being vertical). The flexural strength of masonry, however, is more often governed by the bond between the unit and the mortar: thus when this is the case, the unit flexural strengths will give some indication as to the quality of the unit but not masonry properties.

The strength of a clay unit type is a function of the manufacturing process, the clay mineralogy and the firing/cooling temperature regime. The size and distribution of cores in the unit also influence the various strengths. Single unit compressive strengths of clay units can thus vary between 15 and 150 N mm^{-2}. While geometry also affects the strengths of concrete units, the aggregate, aggregate/cement ratio and water/cement ratio are more influential than the manufacturing process or curing. Block strengths typically vary between about 8 and 40 N mm^{-2}. Calcium silicate units, however, are like clay units in that process affects strength, this time pressure of press and temperature and pressure in the autoclave: initial mix proportions also affect strength. Hence again there is a large range of possible compressive strength, some 5−75 N mm^{-2}.

Moisture and Absorption

The moisture properties of units have considerable effect on the properties of the masonry constructed. The moisture content is the mass of water per unit volume in the unit. The moisture content may be expressed in absolute terms with values in the range of 50−60 kg m^{-3} being typical for units on site; or in relative terms (relative to the density of the unit when dry) with typical values of 2−3 per cent.

The ability of the unit to absorb moisture from the mortar when laid is most commonly assessed by two parameters, the total absorption and the initial rate of absorption (IRA). The total absorption is the amount of water required to saturate the unit — to fill all the pores and voids. Both concrete and fired clay units are porous and total absorption is really a measure of the porosity of the unit.

The IRA is a measure of how quickly a unit could suck water out of a mortar as the masonry is laid. The IRA, or suction, is measured as kg m^{-2} min^{-1}, and is the mass of water absorbed per unit area per unit time. Thus the IRA is a measure related to the pore-size distribution of the unit.

Suction is important in that it helps establish good bond between the unit and the mortar. When mortar is laid on top of a unit, in preparation for the next course, the unit sucks water out of the mortar. As each unit is now laid on the mortar, it also sucks water out of the mortar. Thus the mortar has water sucked out of it by both the units on which it is laid, and the units laid on it! Mortars need some 'water retentivity', as will be seen, in order to hydrate. Units with IRAs in the range $0.5-1.5$ kg m^{-2} min^{-1} will give reasonable bond, but the best bond occurs if the units have a suction (IRA) between 0.8 and 1.2 kg m^{-2} min^{-1} and the mortars are appropriately retentive.[2.7] The appropriateness of a particular mortar to a particular unit may be known by the manufacturer, or if a matter of concern, may have to be determined by experiment. In theory, high suction units can be wetted before laying to improve bond, but it is difficult to monitor or maintain any consistency in the wetting of the units. It is better to choose a compatible mortar and unit — high suction bricks requiring a mortar with high retentivity, for example.

Permanent dimensional changes due to moisture have been mentioned: clay units expand whereas concrete and calcium silicate units shrink. Reversible movement also occurs, with expansion on wetting and shrinkage on drying. For clay masonry (as opposed to clay units) the magnitude of reversible moisture expansion from completely dry to completely saturated is in the range $0.007-0.02$ per cent.[2.8] Typically, reversible moisture movement is not considered in masonry design. Concrete units undergo somewhat larger reversible movements. Many factors affect the magnitude of these and manufacturers may be required to meet limits set in national standards.

Mortar

Mortar is the material used for bonding or jointing the masonry units together. There are thus several important functions for this constituent material to fill.

The mortar must bond the units together so that the masonry as a whole can resist the applied loads. The mortar must have the strength within the masonry to resist the applied compressive loads. The strength of the bond between the mortar and the units is particularly important when flexural loading such as that due to wind is considered. As indicated above, the bond strength depends critically on the competition between the mortar trying to retain its water in order to set and harden, and the unit trying to suck the water out. Typically, minimal suction on the part of the unit, gives low bond strength and too much suction causes the mortar to dehydrate and not to strengthen.

Bond implies more than just flexural strength: it also refers to watertightness. Cracks between mortar and unit are open invitations for water to pass through masonry. A good bond provides a watertight joint to prevent rain penetrating the masonry.

In the fresh state, the mortar has to remain workable so that the mason can lay the units plumb and in line with even regular joints. Units can have slightly different sizes, so the mortar joints must accommodate the variations. Joints should be 10 mm or less in thickness.

Cements

The two major cements used in masonry construction are ordinary Portland cement and lime. 'Masonry cement' is basically a mixture of these two materials, the lime being in the form of finely ground hydrated lime or limestone. The cements (masonry, Portland, lime) are usually combined in set proportions to give mortars of different properties. The lime is normally hydrated lime, but hydraulic lime (lime putty) is sometimes used. Other cements such as pure lime, sulphate-resisting cement, or ordinary Portland cement on its own may be used as conditions warrant.

While 'masonry cements' are mainly mixtures of lime and ordinary Portland cement, there are a few extra additives. These may include air-entraining agents to improve cohesion and the 'fatty' feel of the mortar, a retarder to increase the set-time of the mortar and swelling clays such as bentonite to improve water retentivity. Indeed, the main reason lime is present is to improve workability and water retentivity. Pure lime mortars are very workable, giving the mason plenty of time to lay the unit just so, but they take far too long to set and harden for modern construction demands. Pure Portland cement mortars, on the other hand, lose too much water too quickly to the units and are thus difficult for a mason to work. Also the mortar may well not hydrate with a consequent lack of proper strength gain. Lime and Portland cement are therefore mixed in order to compromise the needs of workability and water retentivity at the construction stage, with the desire for rapid setting, hardening and strength gain for structural load bearing.[2.9] Different proportions are used to meet different demands. Alternatively, it may be permitted to add a 'water thickener' such as methyl cellulose to pure Portland cement mortars to retain the water. The hydration reactions for masonry cements are simply those of Portland cement and lime.

Some additives to mortar are permitted by national standards, typically colouring pigments, plasticizers and retarders. The addition of retarders allows the production of ready-mix mortars in a batching plant off site. There are positive possibilities for quality control in this development, but little is known about the long-term effects of using such mortars.

Sand

Masonry sands are finer than concrete sands. Typical gradation limits are shown in Fig. 2.3. Sands which give the 'fatty' mortars preferred by masons contain more fines than washed sands. Thus their gradation

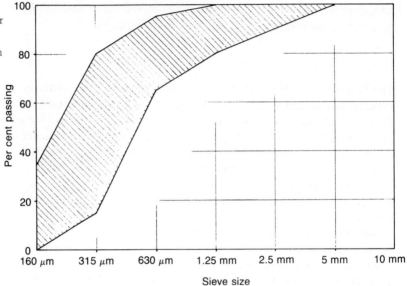

Fig. 2.3 Typical gradation limits for masonry sands with permitted gradations lying in the shaded area

curves tend to lie at the upper edge of the gradation limits shown. If the fines are clay particles, however, an excess may be detrimental to the long-term strength and durability of the masonry. Rather than specify gradation limits, the Australian standard[2.6] takes the approach that any sand may be used in fixed proportions with cements so long as the masonry produced with the resultant mortar meets minimum characteristic compressive and bond strength requirements.

Water

Water used in masonry mortars should be clean: it should not contain anything in sufficient quantity that might harm the masonry or reinforcement. A general rule of thumb is that if you can drink the water, you can make masonry mortar with it. There are often limits on specific salt contents — particularly chlorides which attack reinforcement and prestressing steel quite readily.

Mortar Types

The volume proportions of typical masonry mortars are provided in Table 2.1, together with the sorts of characteristic and average strengths which may be expected from mortars prepared on site. As may be seen, increasing the amount of Portland cement relative to lime gives mortars of higher strength at 28 days. High lime content mortars tend to gain

Table 2.1 Volume proportions of typical mortars for use in reinforced and prestressed masonry. Minimum values of average and characteristic strengths of *site*-prepared mortars are shown to indicate the sorts of strength which may be expected from tests on six cubes at 28 days

Portland cement	Lime	Masonry cement	Sand	Characteristic cube strength at 28 days (N mm^{-2})	Average cube strength at 28 days (N mm^{-2})
1	—	1	5–6	>5	14
$\frac{1}{2}$	—	1	$3\frac{1}{2}$–$4\frac{1}{2}$	>4	9
—	—	1	$2\frac{1}{2}$–3	>2	4
1	1	—	5–6	>1	2.5

strength over much longer periods than low lime content ones, and also tend to give better resistance to rain penetration. The low-strength mortars are thus more preferable for any situation in which the masonry is not highly stressed. The increase in cube strength between the various mortars does not transfer to the masonry: quadrupling the mortar strength is suggested just about to double the masonry strength,[2.10] but other sources indicate even less of an association.[2.9, 2.11]

Compressive strength is not the only criterion by which a mortar should be selected. Workability and retentivity are of at least equal importance and durability should not be ignored. Workability is at best a nebulous term related to the ease with which the mason can work the mortar while constructing the masonry. As indicated in the cements section, as the lime:Portland cement ratio increases, so does the workability — but at the expense of cube strength. Masonry cement mortars owe some of their workability to the high air content which characteristically occurs with such cements. Mortar durability in aggressive environments may usually be increased by increasing the cement content of the mix. In some circumstances special cements like sulphate resistant may be the most appropriate.

Water retentivity can be measured by determining the flow of the mortar on a standard flow table. The mortar is then subjected to some standard suction and the flow measurement repeated. The final flow is expressed as a percentage of the original flow, and called the retentivity. Water retention in the order of 90 per cent is indicative of a good mortar for clay units. Concrete units have lower IRAs in general than clay units, so a mortar with 80 per cent water retentivity may well be acceptable for concrete units.

The first mixing of the cements, sand and water to give a masonry mortar is called tempering. With time, some water will evaporate and the mix will stiffen as initial set develops. Retempering (the addition of more water and thorough remixing) is permitted. There will be some reduction in strength on the first retempering because of the increase in water/cement ratio, but subsequent further additions of water seem to have much less effect. A pot-life of 1½−2 hours is the usual maximum for site-mixed mortars, but ready-mix mortars may well have a longer life (up to 48 hours!). Ready-mix mortars should not be retempered unless permitted by the appropriate specification or standard.

Quality Control

Quality control of mortars on site is not easy. On a cool sunny morning, for example, the mason may not have too much water in the mix. However, as the day progresses and becomes hotter, the IRA of the units may increase as they dry out and water will evaporate faster from the mix. Thus a mid-afternoon mortar batch may contain much more water than the early morning one. Samples of both batches, placed in steel moulds and cured in a carefully controlled environment, will probably have very different strengths, yet the masonry made with the two batches is probably similar in strength.

Again, as site work begins in the morning, or just after lunch, all the masons are requesting mortar. The mixer is working hard and batches are being dumped quite rapidly. How much attention is being paid to the standard which requires a minimum mixing time of 3 minutes? Of course once all the mortar boards are replete, and there is some mortar in reserve, the mixer might chug away for half an hour before the batch is dumped, well beyond the maximum mixing time specified in the standard!

A final example would be the energetic young labourer whose 20 shovelfuls of sand first thing in the morning are very different in volume from the 20 in the late afternoon. Nevertheless, quality control of site-produced mortars is best assured by a proportion specification.[2.5, 2.6] The proportions of the materials in the mortar can be assessed and problems rectified quite quickly — much more rapidly than with a 7-day or 28-day strength specification. Quality control of site-produced mortars also involves inducing a willingness and understanding on the part of the masons and their labourers that consistent good quality is crucial. Since it is the masonry which is of importance, it would perhaps be better to perform some quality control tests at this stage on samples of the masonry, as well as the mortar. Tests on the latter alone just give a measure of the consistency of the mortar from the beginning to the end of the job. Some tests on the former will give some indication of how well the materials are going together during the job.

Retarded mortars produced in a batching plant and delivered to the job site can be assessed by sampling at the plant and/or the job site.

Strength or proportions can be specified: the manufacturer should be able to control the variability of both parameters to within reasonable limits. Samples at the job site should be taken at both the beginning and end of use of a batch. As with site-produced mortar, since it is the masonry which matters, some of these samples should perhaps be of the masonry. Retarded mortars should only be used within the period of useful life specified by the manufacturer.

Grout

Grout may be thought of as a fluid concrete mix and is used to fill cores in hollow masonry or wall cavities created in the masonry to contain reinforcement or post-tensioning/prestressing wires. It should not be confused with the special grouts used to bond anchoring bolts and the like into concrete structures. The purpose of grout in masonry is to provide some additional compressive strength to the masonry, and more importantly, to connect the masonry and the reinforcement such that composite action can occur. There is, therefore, a prime requirement of grout that it fill the cavity completely, bonding the masonry and the steel together and acting as cover for the steel: the masonry cannot be guaranteed to be watertight. The strength of the grout has to be sufficient to transmit load between steel and masonry; thus a minimum characteristic compressive strength in the order of $10-15$ N mm^{-2} is appropriate.

To fulfil its prime purpose, the grout must be highly workable when poured, and be 'self-compactible'. Thus a slump of $225-250$ mm is desirable. Since the cavities being filled are often restricted, both by unit geometry and the presence of reinforcement, it becomes imperative to have the cavities clean before pouring the grout. Projections of mortar for example, should be removed so that the flow of grout is not impeded, and the effective steel cover is not reduced. The cover provided by the masonry can be taken as zero. Also, consideration should be given to the maximum size of aggregate specified.

Typically when the grout space has a least horizontal dimension of 50 mm or less, a fine grout should be used. The fine aggregate should

Table 2.2 Typical mix proportions for coarse and fine grouts

Grout	Portland cement	Fine aggregate	Coarse aggregate
Fine	1	2.5–3.5	
Coarse	1	2.5–3.5	1.5–2.5

be a sand with a top size of 5 mm. When the cavity is larger than 50 mm in its least dimension, a coarse grout can be used. Here a top-size particle limit of 14 mm is suggested.

The desired workability should not be achieved through a high water content if avoidable: addition of a superplasticizer shortly before placing should be considered. Grouts with high water contents will want to shrink away from the surrounding masonry in time. Internal stresses will develop and may even cause the two materials to separate.

Grout is usually assessed through slump measurements and/or compression tests on cylinders.

Masonry Properties

The mechanical properties of masonry of interest to an engineer designing reinforced or prestressed masonry are those of deformation and strength — just as with concrete. There are many similarities in the behaviour of the two materials but also some significant differences. The fact there are similarities should not be surprising. Like concrete, masonry is good at resisting compression, not so good at resisting pure shear, and not very good at all at resisting tension. Thus, when resisting structural actions that induce shear, reinforcement is frequently needed. Actions such as flexure which induce tension of any magnitude invariably require the masonry to be reinforced or post-tensioned. Post-tensioning increases the cracking moment of resistance of a structural masonry element, and thus its serviceability and resistance to flexure.[2.12] Masonry constructed from all types of units[2.13–2.15] may be post-tensioned with tendons running through pockets formed in the masonry or cores in the units themselves. All these attributes are similar to concrete.

Further, concrete units jointed together with a Portland cement based mortar should be expected to creep under compressive load and shrink — as does plain concrete. Clay masonry will also creep, but expands rather than shrinks: expansion may be treated as a negative shrinkage.[2.16] Under distributed or concentrated compressive loading perpendicular to the bed plane, solid masonry fails like concrete,[2.17,2.18] whereas face-shell bedded hollow masonry fails in a completely different manner, as explained later. In direct tension or flexure, the bed planes of all masonry become planes of weakness. The mortar joints in fact are a major cause of the anisotropic behaviour of masonry, a distinct difference from concrete behaviour. As long as the designer is aware of the differences in behaviour, he may discriminate as to when and which of the concepts and procedures used in reinforced and prestressed concrete design can be applied to masonry.

Deformation

'Elastic' Deformation

As with concrete, the initial deformation of masonry subjected to load is called the elastic deformation. Empirical relationships between the compressive modulus of elasticity E, perpendicular to the bed plane and the equivalent compressive strength are usually assumed. For lower-strength masonry, the relationship is usually taken as linear:

$$E_m = \alpha f'_m.$$

The factor α varies between 600 and 1000,[2.5, 2.6, 2.10] depending on the tests or national code being considered and whether the units are clay, concrete or calcium silicate; f'_m is the design compressive strength. In codes of practice an upper limit is usually placed on the value of E_m for higher-strength masonry.

The actual stress–strain behaviour of masonry subjected to compression perpendicular to the bed plane is depicted in Fig. 2.4. With clay units, strong mortars tend to produce masonry of almost linear brittle behaviour, whereas the weaker mortars tend to produce masonry with a behaviour more akin to concrete: it is possible to observe strain softening and a post-peak descending branch. Thus for ultimate strength design, a triangular, parabolic or rectangular stress block could be used.

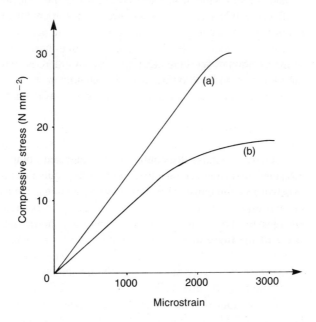

Fig. 2.4 Typical stress–strain curves for solid clay masonry with (a) a strong structural mortar, and (b) a weak one

Viscous Deformation

Masonry creeps but there is very little information on the magnitude of the effect. Some short-term data (about one year) are available and some of these have been extrapolated for long-term estimates.[2.16, 2.19] Codes of practice are beginning to include guidance for creep, but the values of creep coefficient (creep strain/initial elastic strain) provided are usually low — in the order of 1.0–3.0.[2.10] These values are similar to the short-term data but considerably less than the long-term estimates based on one set of short-term data: 5.0–6.0 for clay masonry and up to 10.0 for concrete masonry.[2.19] Long-term values of such magnitude have not been confirmed experimentally or in practice. However, in the longest monitoring of a building, creep strains almost three times the initial strain were measured in clay brick walls in a 10-storey-high building after 5 years of live loading.[2.20]

Lower values of creep coefficient are associated with clay units and larger ones with concrete units. This is quite reasonable given that clay units hardly creep at all in comparison with concrete units. Creep in clay masonry occurs mainly through creep in the mortar joints. Different mortar types creep different amounts, with 'weaker' mortars showing greater propensities for creep.[2.16] Specific creep in a 'weak' mortar has been shown to be about 1000 $\mu\epsilon$ per N mm^{-2} at 3 weeks, rising to 1250 $\mu\epsilon$ per N mm^{-2} at one year.

Many of the factors which affect creep in concrete can also be expected to affect creep in masonry: temperature, relative humidity, age of loading, magnitude of loading. Most tests have been performed on drying specimens, loaded at 28 days of age. Although there is clearly a dearth of information concerning creep in masonry, there is some guidance in the literature on how to deal with the phenomenon.[2.21, 2.22] Long-term differential movement should be given due consideration.

Moisture Movements

All types of masonry are subject to moisture-related movement, some permanent and some reversible. In clay masonry, the free permanent moisture expansion is typically some 50–90 per cent of the unrestrained expansion of the units.[2.23, 2.24] The shrinkage of the mortar counteracts the expansion of the clay units to some degree. The differential movement between the two components of the masonry can result in some fine cracking of strong mortars but is thought to be relieved in the weaker mortars by creep. In some cases, walls expanded more than the units from which they were made.[2.23, 2.24] Sulphate expansion of the mortar was thought to be involved.

The magnitude of unrestrained 5-year expansion of clay masonry, can be classified like the movements of the units themselves into high, medium or low:

Low   growth $\leq$ 350 $\mu\epsilon$
Medium 350 $\mu\epsilon$ $\leq$ growth $\leq$ 700 $\mu\epsilon$
High   700 $\mu\epsilon$ $\leq$ growth

The highest 5-year growth is thought to be in the order of 1250 $\mu\epsilon$, and in a 10 m length of wall, this would give a permanent horizontal expansion of 12.5 mm. Expansions of about 2000 $\mu\epsilon$ have been reported for walls 6[2.25] and 7[2.26] years old. If ignored, even half these levels of expansion can easily cause structural distress. For example, in one extreme experiment,[2.27] a trial 63 foot long clay brick wall built without expansion joints from kiln fresh units expanded and broke pillars abutting the ends of the wall in 10 days. A similar wall built from similar units soaked for 5 weeks prior to wall construction took 30 days to repeat the effect. Manufacturers should be able to provide 5-year permanent expansion data for their clay units, and expansion of masonry can hence be estimated.

Reversible moisture movement in clay masonry between completely dry and saturated states lies in the range 0.007–0.02 per cent (70–200 $\mu\epsilon$).[2.8] The variation is due in part to the different types of clay unit and in part to differences in method of test.

Reversible moisture movement in concrete masonry is considerably higher as shown in Table 2.3.[2.28] Permanent shrinkage in concrete masonry is generally in the range 350–600 $\mu\epsilon$. Some of the shrinkage is due to carbonation. There is a multitude of factors which can affect both permanent and reversible shrinkage, so detailed information should be obtained from the manufacturer if necessary (and available!).

Thermal Movement

The coefficient of thermal expansion of clay masonry is in the range $6-8 \times 10^{-6}$ °C^{-1}, but for concrete masonry the range is somewhat larger, being $6-13 \times 10^{-6}$ °C^{-1}. Thermal expansion/contraction may be seen vertically in masonry, but horizontal movement is typically

Table 2.3 Reversible moisture movement in different types of concrete masonry

Unit type	Curing condition	Reversible shrinkage (%)	($\mu\epsilon$)
Normal-weight brick or block	Air	0.02–0.05	200–500
Lightweight	Air	0.04–0.08	400–800
Lightweight	Autoclave	0.02–0.06	200–600
Aerated	Air	0.08–0.20	800–2000
Aerated	Autoclave	0.05–0.09	500–900
Calcium silicate	Autoclave	0.01–0.04	200–400

restrained and large thermal contractions tend to cause fine cracks to develop between units and mortar in the head joints.[2.8]

Compressive Strength

Mechanisms of Failure

Solid Masonry Masonry is usually compressed perpendicular to the bed plane, as this is where masonry exhibits its greatest compressive strength. For completely solid units, the strength parallel to the bed plane is about half that perpendicular to the bed plane.[2.29] With cellular or perforated units, the ratio can fall to a third.

Mortar tends to be more flexible than the unit, i.e. has a lower initial modulus (or modulus of elasticity). Thus in unrestrained masonry, mortar tends to want to expand more than the unit due to Poisson's effect.[2.30] As mortar and unit are bonded together the unit resists the desired extra lateral expansion of the mortar. The mortar in the bed joint is thus subject to triaxial compression: the unit to compression perpendicular to the bed joint and bilateral tension. These states of stress develop in masonry which is unrestrained laterally — like the central unit of a five high or larger stack-bonded brick prism. The lateral stresses are not high but are sufficient to increase the strength of the mortar beyond its uniaxial value, and to have some effect on the magnitude of the ultimate compressive strength of the masonry.[2.11, 2.17]

A masonry wall, however, may well be restrained at its ends by piers and/or at the top and bottom by a foundation, floor slab or capping beam. These restraints will resist the desired Poisson expansion of the wall and may well induce lateral compression in the direction of wall length. The units therefore may be subject to lateral tension only in the width direction of the masonry leaf (wythe). The intimate details of the local stress states in masonry components are not well understood.

The lateral stresses in the unit were at one time thought to be the cause of failure of masonry. More recently, the similarity of failure between concrete and masonry under similar uniaxial and biaxial stress conditions (Figs 2.5 and 2.6) has led to the belief that the cause of failure in the material is the same.[2.17, 2.32] As compressive stress flows around flaws or voids in the material, lateral tension develops (Fig. 2.7). The magnitudes of these lateral tensions are much larger than those due to material interaction. Strength ratios in different stress states predicted from these flaw stresses correlate well with experimentally determined strengths of the materials.[2.33]

In solid, single-leaf walls subject to relatively uniform compression, cracks develop along the edges of head joints and extend through the

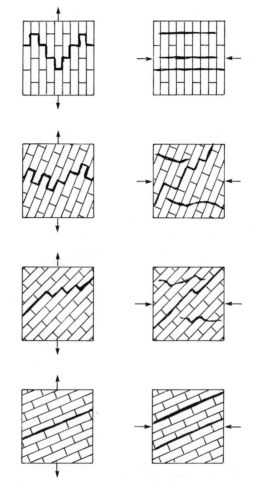

Fig. 2.5 Fracture patterns in uniaxial tension and uniaxial compression for concrete as depicted by Vile,[2.31] and masonry stressed at various angles to the bedding plane (0°, 22.5°, 45°, 67.5° and 90°) as depicted by Page.[2.29] Note the weak bed planes affect the precise fracture pattern but in general both materials crack perpendicular to tension and parallel to compression

units above and below. As load increases, so do the lengths of the cracks. However, failure occurs with the wall splitting in its own plane (Fig. 2.6), the cracks which cause this not being visible prior to failure. Stack-bonded prisms and wallettes of masonry — the small specimens usually tested to determine masonry strength — fail in the same plane. A masonry

Fig. 2.6 Fracture patterns in biaxial stress states for concrete as depicted by Vile,[2.31] and masonry as depicted by Page.[2.29] In biaxial compression, both materials crack in the plane of compression. In biaxial tension–compression, they crack parallel to the compression, perpendicular to the tension. For concrete, a transition zone is noted, involving both fracture modes when one stress is high compression and the other low compression or tension

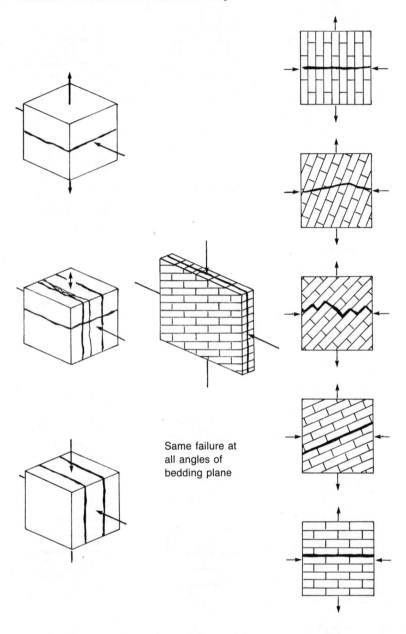

Same failure at all angles of bedding plane

pier or column, however, fails differently.[2.11] The cracks which develop through the head joints extend and expand, eventually causing failure. The geometry of the masonry therefore affects the strength measured, piers being stronger than walls.

When subject to concentrated load, solid masonry walls fail in the same

Applied compressive stress

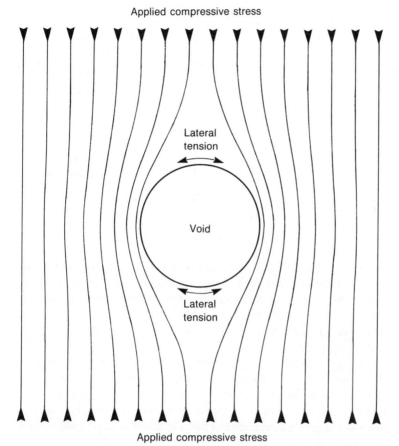

Applied compressive stress

Fig. 2.7 As compressive stress flows around a void or flaw in a material, lateral tension develops in the material at the top and bottom of the void. This tension causes the material to crack parallel to the applied compression

way as does a similarly loaded concrete slab. A crack develops in the masonry in the line of the concentrated load some way beneath the bearing plate, and extends along the line of the load until failure occurs.[2.18]

   Face-shell Bedded Hollow Masonry As the name implies, in this type of masonry, mortar is only laid on the face-shells of hollow blocks. Indeed, the geometry of many hollow units is such that the webs do not align vertically from course to course in running bond construction, and full bedding defaults automatically to face-shell load bearing.

   Like a solid masonry wall, a hollow masonry wall fails by splitting in its own plane. The cause, however, is entirely different, with the webs of the hollow unit being split by a double deep-beam action.[2.34] This action produces stresses across the centre of the webs as depicted in Fig. 2.8. It is the tensile stresses at the top and bottom which cause the webs of the block to split. The type of mortar has no effect on the splitting

Tension ¦ Compression

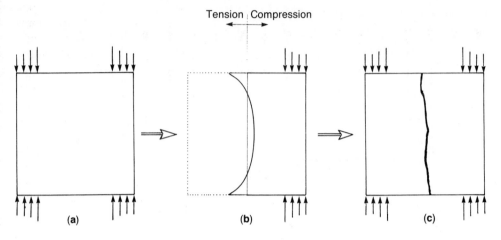

(a)   (b)   (c)

Fig. 2.8 The vertical cross-section of a face-shell bedded hollow masonry unit under axial compressive load shown in (a) includes a web. Due to a double deep-beam action,[2.34] the centre line of the web is subject to lateral tension at tis top and bottom and lateral compression in the middle, (b). This causes the apparently unloaded web to split up the centre line as in (c)

mechanism, but final failure of face-shell bedded hollow masonry also involves some crushing of the mortar as the two halves of the masonry buckle out. Thus very much stronger mortars give only very slightly stronger masonry (less than 10 per cent increase in masonry strength with over a twofold increase in mortar strength from that of a 'weak' structural mortar).[2.35]

Under concentrated loading, the same thing happens: the masonry splits in its own plane.[2.36] This is entirely different from the failure of solid masonry described above. There is some enhancement of load on the basis of loaded length ratio, as opposed to loaded area ratio, but the effect of most of the other parameters known to affect strength enhancement in solid masonry is not known. The presence of a bond beam to distribute load on to the hollow masonry beneath has a beneficial effect but the angle of load dispersion is less than the usually assumed 45°. In the only tests performed to date, the angle of dispersion in 200 mm deep bond beams was found to be 30°, and 25° in 400 mm deep beams.[2.37] Eccentricity of load application by one-sixth of the wall width reduced load capacity by 25 per cent. Thus if hollow masonry is to be prestressed, a capping block or spreader beam is recommended to improve load transfer to the masonry.

Grouted Masonry When hollow masonry is grouted, the compressive strength of the combination is usually less than the strengths of the individual components.[2.35] Nevertheless, the load to cause failure is higher in the grouted case because of the increase in load-bearing cross-sectional area. Under compressive loading the face-shells of the masonry typically split away from the grout cores. The cause of this is thought to be a wedging action of the grout, the wedge shape developing because of the taper of the cores of the hollow units.[2.38, 2.39] The difference in material stiffness between grout and unit causes the grout wedge to create lateral tensile stresses in the face-shells when the masonry is compressed. The face-shells then split away from the rest of the masonry.

Grouted solid masonry is somewhat different. Here, typically, cavities in the units are not filled, but cavities are created in the masonry. Cavity, diaphragm and fin walls all contain spaces within or between sections of solid masonry, as may piers. There is little in the literature about the failure of such masonry when unreinforced. Reinforced masonry, however, behaves similarly to reinforced concrete in most instances.[2.40,2.41]

Factors Affecting Compressive Strength

The compressive strength of masonry is dependent on both the mortar and unit type, but not on a 1:1 ratio with the strength of either component. Typical ranges of results for different units and mortars are shown in Figs 2.9–2.12. However, these do not differentiate between the different unit manufacturing processes and geometry: a pressed unit for example can give higher masonry strength than an extruded unit of higher unit strength. Tabulated values of masonry strength in a code of practice, based on unit strength and mortar type, must be conservative by their very nature. Thus it is perhaps better to determine the characteristic strength of the masonry selected by test rather than by code.

Workmanship also affects strength with many factors being involved.[2.1, 2.2] Not laying the units plumb and square can reduce strength by 15 per cent; whereas improper filling of the vertical head (perpend) joints, indicative of poor workmanship, has been shown not to reduce strength significantly.[2.1] Overzealous furrowing of bed joints

Fig. 2.9 Typical range of masonry characteristic compressive strength versus single unit strength for solid and perforated clay units with structural mortars nominally of (a) 10 N mm^{-2} and (b) 20 N mm^{-2} strength

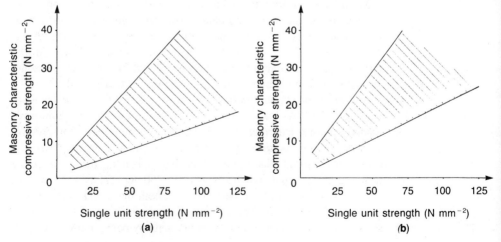

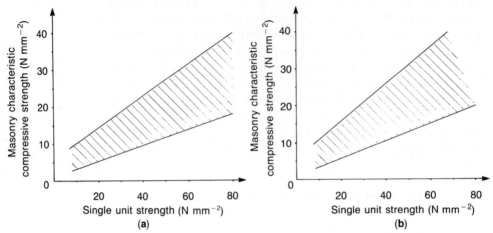

Fig. 2.10 Typical range of masonry characteristic compressive strength versus single unit strength for calcium silicate units with structural mortars nominally of (a) 10 N mm⁻² and (b) 20 N mm⁻² strength

will also reduce strength because supposedly fully bedded solid units end up being essentially face-shell bedded. Variations in joint thickness can cause variation in strength: thinner joints produce stronger masonry. Moving the units after laying, improper curing, the list can go on. The net result of workmanship is that it affects the variability of the masonry constructed.

Masonry is bound to be variable to some degree because its component materials are. The approach used in most codes of practice of using characteristic values of properties like compressive strength is a recognition of the variable nature of the material. Good workmanship may not increase inherent variability of the masonry, but poor workmanship certainly can. Good workmanship can be achieved on site — including consistent mortar preparation — but needs some effort.

Masonry gains strength with age after construction, as does concrete, particularly as the mortar hardens. However, removal of moisture by the units may reduce or even stop hydration, and strength gain is probably slow thereafter. Most testing of masonry is performed at 28 days. Mortar cube strength certainly changes between 7 and 28 days, and masonry strength has been shown to increase slightly in that period.[2.42]

A final factor known to influence masonry strength is eccentricity of loading.[2.42–2.44] As load is applied away from the centre of a uniformly loaded wall or prism, there is often an apparent increase in compressive strength.[2.44] The compressive strength is computed on the basis of a linear stress—strain relationship and engineers' bending theory. Increases in strength so computed in the range of 15—60 per cent over the uniaxial compressive strength have been found in both brick and blockwork at an eccentricity of $t/3$. The computed increase could result from the stress—strain behaviour of the masonry actually being non-linear, from

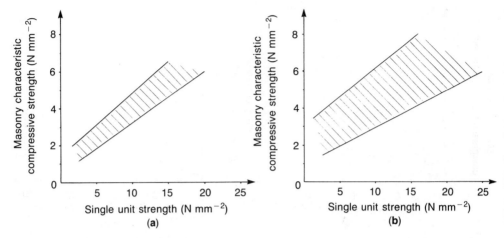

(a)   (b)

Fig. 2.11 Typical range of masonry characteristic compressive strength versus single unit strength for lightweight and aerated solid concrete units with mortars nominally of (a) 5 N mm^{-2} and (b) 10 N mm^{-2} strength

there being a smaller volume of material being highly compressed (and thus a smaller volume to contain the critical voids for failure), or a combination thereof.

Bond and Flexural Bond Strength

The two aspects of bond — watertightness and flexural bond strength — are tied together to some degree. Units and mortar which are strongly bonded together will resist rain penetration better than a combination which has cracks along the interface of the two components. The latter will also have a predisposition to fail at a low flexural stress. However, even while there is a general trend, good watertightness does not always go hand in hand with high bond strength.[2.7]

When the suction from the unit is well balanced by the water retentivity of the mortar, good bond will generally result. There has to be some movement of water from the mortar to the unit to create good bond, but it is not clear why. Too much movement of water dehydrates the mortar which subsequently does not gain strength, with a concomitant result of low flexural bond strength. Bond appears to be achieved through adhesion of mortar constituents to those of the unit by secondary polar bonding, and by mechanical keying of the relatively rough unit surface with crystals from the mortar constituents growing into the surface pits and capillaries of the unit. With an 'ancient' lime mortar, there is also thought to have been some chemical interaction between the unit and the mortar.[2.45] Generally, the more lime in a mortar, the better is the resistance to rain penetration.

Many properties of both mortars and units have been studied in respect of their effect on bond strength.[2.7] In mortar, water retentivity is thought

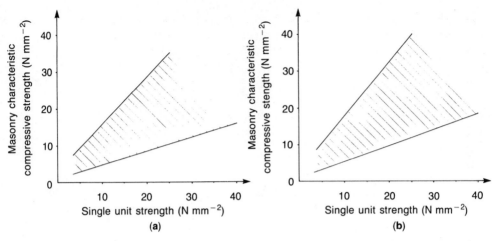

Fig. 2.12 Typical range of masonry characteristic compressive strength versus single unit strength for hollow face-shell-bedded concrete masonry units with mortars nominally of (a) 5 N mm^{-2} and (b) 10 N mm^{-2} strength

to be most important. Generally a mortar with high retentivity will give a watertight joint with low absorbency units. As the absorbency of the unit increases, the mortar should be less retentive to achieve a similar watertightness.

Of unit properties, those dealing with the rate and quantity of moisture which a unit can absorb have been studied most. Factors related to absorption (the total amount of water that can be absorbed) and the suction (the IRA) have been studied. With different units different parameters appear to be important, but the IRA of the unit is generally thought of as being the most important. The moisture content of the unit is usually only important if the unit is saturated before laying and thereby does not suck any moisture from the unit.

Typically tests on the effect of the various parameters associated with mortars and units on the bond between the two have involved varying one parameter while keeping others 'constant'. On site, however, many of the parameters would be varying simultaneously. The approach of varying one parameter at a time does not indicate which parameter is most important when many are varying. One such study[2.46] revealed some unexpected effects, with mortar joint thickness being found to be the most important parameter with respect to bond strength. Thinner joints provided higher bond strengths than thicker ones.

Mean bond strengths are typically less than 1.0 N mm^{-2}, more usually in the order of 0.5 N mm^{-2}. Measuring techniques include the flexural testing of wallettes of masonry, beam testing of stack-bonded prisms, and bond-wrench. In this latter test, the units on either side of a joint are clamped in an apparatus, and then the joint is flexed. It is a simple method of determining flexural bond strength but produces highly variable results, due in part to the clamping system being so close to the joint being tested.

Age affects bond strength, with some studies showing a loss of strength with age with masonry cement mortars and a gain with Portland cement/lime mortars[2.46, 2.47] and another showing increased strength with both types of mortar.[2.48] Different flexural strengths occur when masonry is flexed in and out of plane. Out-of-plane flexure would occur for example in a wall subject to wind loading, whereas in-plane flexure would develop in a shear wall. In design, it would seem appropriate to assume masonry has no tensile flexural capacity!

Shear Strength

Shear stresses are often applied to masonry in conjunction with normal stress as shown in Fig. 2.13(a). The mode of failure which occurs depends on the relative magnitude of the shear and normal stresses. With low normal stress what is called stepping or friction failure may occur as shown in Fig. 2.13(b). This mode of failure produces the steep line (i) of the failure envelope shown in Fig. 2.13(d). Results for this type of failure have been expressed in a Coulomb type of failure criterion.[2.49,2.50]

$$v = v_0 + \mu f.$$

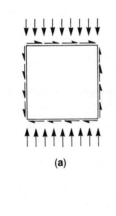

(a)

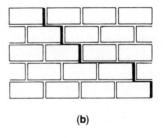

(b)

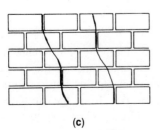

(c)

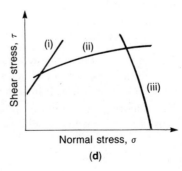

Normal stress, σ

(d)

Fig. 2.13 Normal and shear stress occur in combination in masonry, in shear walls, for example. A typical result is shown in (a). Stepping or friction failure may occur (b), or 'brick cracking' (c). A schematic of the failure envelope is shown in (d): curve (i) is associated with the failure mode in (b); curve (ii) with that in (c); and curve (iii) with compression failure

v is the shear stress at failure, when normal stress f is applied; μ is a coefficient of friction and has been found to vary from about 0.3 to about 1.1. The value of μ has been related to the proportion of head joints which open during failure, rather than just being the coefficient of friction in the bed plane. v_0 is the shear strength with no normal stress applied: results fall in the range $0.1-0.7$ N mm^{-2}. Results from various researchers show considerable differences.[2.49] In instances where friction failure is not observed,[2.49] the intercept for line (i) on the v-axis of Fig. 2.13(d) must be higher than the intercept for line (ii).

Line (ii) is associated with the mode of failure depicted in Fig. 2.13(c), 'brick cracking'. In this case cracks pass through some head joints, but generally progress through the masonry at some angle to the bedding plane. Again, with some types of masonry, this mode of failure has not been observed.[2.50] Failure criteria developed for this mode are linear[2.50] or parabolic,[2.49] e.g.:

$$ v = \frac{f_t}{2.3} \sqrt{\left(1 + \frac{f}{f_t}\right)}. $$

The third type of failure is straight compressive failure and occurs under high values of applied normal stress. This mode provides curve (iii) of the failure envelope of Fig. 2.13(d).

Codes of practice typically deal with modes (i) and (ii) with a single Coulomb criterion. One or two values of shear stress v_0 are allowed depending on the type of masonry. The magnitude of the design characteristic value can be a multiple of the characteristic compressive[2.5] or tensile[2.6] strength of the masonry. Coefficients of friction in such codes of practice vary widely from 0.1 to 0.3.[2.51] Maximum limits are usually applied to the characteristic shear strength. Nevertheless, as the wall geometry and method of load application in a test have been shown to influence results of shear tests,[2.51] the applicability of a generalized $v-f$ failure criterion is questionable. Variation in material properties (shear and tensile bond strength, compressive strength) caused considerable variability in the derived $v-f$ relatioinships,[2.51] and conservatism in code formulations remains justified until greater understanding of failure under shear loading is achieved.

Durability

The durability of masonry depends on the durability of the components, the workmanship, the detailing and the maintenance of the masonry. Some units perform well in some environments, but not in others.[2.52] The majority of durability problems arise from the presence of moisture.[2.53] Units may spall if subject to freeze−thaw conditions when close to saturation. The cause of spalling is probably similar to that of concrete.

Efflorescence is another problem. Unsightly white stains appear on the masonry as salts leach out of the mortar, out of concrete units, or are soaked up from the ground. The most common leachant is lime and if left on the masonry, it will slowly convert to calcium carbonate through reaction with carbon dioxide. This may cause problems for the masonry as the crystallization of calcium carbonate from solution is an expansive reaction. Crystals which form in the surface pores and capillaries of the masonry may degrade and disrupt the surface layer. Without visible efflorescence, it is difficult to determine whether spalling in brickwork is due to salt crystallization, freeze—thaw action or stress concentration in the masonry.[2.53]

Jointing can have a major influence on masonry durability; weather joints are best because they shed the water out of the joints and down the face of masonry. Detailing is important in order to avoid water collecting on parts of the masonry. The most durable masonry is thin jointed, as plenty of structures from the past indicate — the Pyramids, many places of worship, castles, walls and aqueducts. Of more recent structures, those built with thin joints seem less prone to serviceability problems than others.

Reinforcement and Prestressing/ Post-tensioning Tendons

Reinforcing or prestressing steel should meet the requirements of the national standard. Typically in reinforced masonry, standard rebar or stainless steel has been used. Galvanized bars should be avoided, as problems in the UK revealed that hydrogen embrittlement weakens the bars by encouraging surface crack propagation.[2.54] Plain non-protected bars have served well in reinforced masonry as have epoxy-covered, taped and painted bars. Stress—strain behaviour is taken as ideal elasto-plastic or linear elastic up to one level of stress, then linear elastic to yield but with a lower modulus and ideally plastic after yield.

In post-tensioned masonry, various methods have been used to provide protection to the tendons against corrosive action. In New Zealand, post-tensioning cables were housed in garden hose,[2.55] well sealed at the ends. Standard prestressing wires in ducts embedded in grout were used in the UK.[2.56] More recently Macalloy high-tensile bars[2.13-2.15] have been used, with protection being provided either by plastic ducts[2.13] or by treating the rods and couplers with Denso paste (a proprietary product) and wrapping in Denso tape (another proprietary product).[2.14, 2.15] In Switzerland, a modular system involving grease and plastic ducts[2.57] has been used to protect the post-tensioning steel. All these options appear to have been successful in providing protection to date.

Summary

The properties of masonry can vary widely given the choices of unit and mortar. Some inherent variability in masonry must be expected from the manufacturing processes of the units — clay, calcium silicate or concrete. The quality and variability of structural masonry depend not only on the quality of the component materials but also the workmanship in putting them together. Thus masonry behaviour cannot be assessed fully from the properties of the component materials alone: good materials give the possibility of good masonry.

Masonry is strong in compression and thus requires reinforcement in structural elements required to resist tensile stresses on part of their section. Prestressing, usually achieved through post-tensioning, takes advantage of the compressive strength of masonry and improves serviceability by reducing or eliminating cracking. Various techniques have been used successfully to date to protect prestressing wires/post-tensioning rods.

References

2.1   Hendry A W 1976 The effect of site factors on masonry performance. In Jessop E L, Ward M A (eds) *Proceedings of the First Canadian Masonry Symposium* Calgary June 1976 pp 182—98

2.2   West H W H (ed) 1988 Masonry (3). *Proceedings of the British Masonry Society Symposium on Workmanship in Masonry Construction*. Also in *Masonry International* 1988 **2**(1): 1—15; **2**(2): 35—6; **2**(3): 71—86

2.3   Ramaswamy G S 1952 Prestressing an assembly of stone blocks by post-tensioning. *Indian Concrete Journal* **27**(12): 450

2.4   Taylor J B 1961 Prestressed granite masonry for a retaining wall. *Civil Engineering* ASCE, **31**(1): 33—4

2.5   Canadian Standards Association 1984 *Masonry Design for Buildings* CAN3-S304-M84, 69pp

2.6   Standards Association of Australia 1988 *Masonry in Buildings* AS 3700-1988, 45pp

2.7   Goodwin J F, West H W H 1982 A review of the literature on brick/mortar bond. *Proceedings of the British Ceramic Society* **30**: 23—37

2.8   Jessop E L 1980 Moisture, thermal, elastic and creep properties in masonry: a state of the art report. In Suter G T, Keller, H (eds) *Proceedings of the Second Canadian Masonry Symposium* Ottawa June 1980 pp 505—20

2.9   Davison J I 1976 Mortar technology. In Jessop E L, Ward M A (eds) *Proceedings of the First Canadian Masonry Symposium* Calgary June 1976 pp 12—21

2.10   British Standards Institution 1985 *Use of Masonry Part 2 Structural Use of Reinforced and Prestressed Masonry* BS 5628, 46pp

2.11   Shrive N G, Jessop E L 1982 An examination of the failure mechanisms of masonry piers, prisms and walls subjected to compression. In West H W H (ed) *Proceedings of the British Ceramic Society* **30**: 110−17

2.12   Curtin W G 1982 Development, application and potential of reinforced and prestressed masonry. In *Reinforced and Prestressed Masonry* Institution of Civil Engineers, Thomas Telford Ltd, London pp 1−12

2.13   Bradshaw R E, Drinkwater J P 1982 Reinforced brickwork in the George Armitage office block, Robin Hood, Wakefield. In *Reinforced and Prestressed Masonry* Institution of Civil Engineers, Thomas Telford Ltd, London pp 13−22

2.14   Curtin W G, Shaw G, Beck J K, Pope L S 1982 Post-tensioned free cantilever diaphragm wall project. In Laterconsult (ed) *Proceedings of the Sixth International Brick Masonry Conference* Andil, Rome pp 1645−56

2.15   Shaw G, Othick G J, Priestley C L 1986 *The Orsborn Memorial Halls at Boscombe* Engineers File No 6 Brick Development Association, UK 14pp

2.16   Ameny P, Loov R E, Shrive N G 1984 Models for long-term deformation of brickwork. *Masonry International* **1**: 27−36

2.17   Shrive N G 1983 A fundamental approach to the fracture of masonry. In Longworth J, Warwaruk J (eds) *Proceedings of the Third Canadian Masonry Symposium* Edmonton June 1983 pp 4.1−16

2.18   Page A W, Hendry A W 1988 Design rules for concentrated loads on masonry. *The Structural Engineer* **66**(17): 273−81

2.19   Shrive N G, England G L 1981 Elastic, creep and shrinkage behaviour of masonry. *The International Journal of Masonry Construction* **1**(3) : 103−9

2.20   Lenczner D 1986 *In situ* measurement of creep movement in a brick masonry tower block. *Masonry International* **8**: 17−20

2.21   Lenczner D 1981 Brickwork: a guide to creep. *International Journal of Masonry Construction* **1**(4): 127−33

2.22   Shrive N G 1988 Effects of time dependent movements in composite and post-tensioned masonry. *Masonry International* **2**(1): 25−9

2.23   Smith R G 1974 Moisture expansion of structural ceramics; expansion of unrestrained fletton brickwork. *Transactions of the British Ceramic Society* **73**(6): 191

2.24   Brooks J J, Bingel P R 1988 Moisture expansion of fletton brickwork. In West H W H (ed) *Proceedings of the British Masonry Society* **2**: 8−11

2.25   Beard R, Dinnie A, Richard R 1969 Movement of brickwork: I Experimental unrestrained walls of fletton bricks. *Transactions of the British Ceramic Society* **68**(2): 73

2.26   Hosking J S 1964 *Prevention of Damage due to Moisture Expansion in Ceramic Structures.* Commonwealth Scientific and Industrial Research Organization Reprint CIB, 1, UDC 699.82

2.27   Hosking J S, Hueber H V 1962 *Dimensional Changes due to Moisture in Bricks and Brickwork* Special Technical Publication 320 American Society for Testing and Materials

2.28   Baker L R, Jessop E L 1982 Moisture movement in concrete masonry: a review. The International Journal of Masonry Construction 2(2): 75–80

2.29   Page A W 1982 An experimental investigation of the biaxial strength of brick masonry. *Proceedings of the Sixth International Brick Masonry Conference* Andil, Rome pp 3–15

2.30   Hilsdorf H K 1969 Investigation into the failure mechanism of brick masonry loaded in axial compression. In Johnson F B (ed) *Designing, Engineering and Constructing with Masonry Products* Gulf Publishing, Houston pp 34–41

2.31   Vile G W D 1968 The strength of concrete under short-term static biaxial stress. In Brooks A E, Newman K (eds) *The Structure of Concrete and its Behaviour under Load, Proceedings of an International Conference* London Sept 1965 Cement and Concrete Association pp 275–88

2.32   Shrive N G, El Rahman M 1985 Understanding the cause of cracking in concrete: a diagnostic aid. *Concrete International* 7(5): 39–44

2.33   El Rahman M, Shrive N G 1984 Crack initiation in multiaxial compressive stress fields. *Proceedings of International Conference on Concrete under Multiaxial Conditions* Toulouse May 1984 RILEM-CEB-CNRS 1 pp 220–9

2.34   Shrive N G 1982 The failure mechanism of face-shell bedded (ungrouted and unreinforced) masonry. *The International Journal of Masonry Construction* 2(3): 115–28

2.35   Drysdale R G, Hamid A A 1979 Behaviour of concrete block masonry under axial compression. *Journal of the American Concrete Institute* 76: 707–21

2.36   Page A W, Shrive N G, Jessop E L 1987 Concentrated loads on hollow masonry — a pilot study. *Masonry International* 1(2): 58–61

2.37   Page A W, Shrive N G 1990 Concentrated loads on hollow concrete masonry. *American Concrete Institute Structural Journal* 87(4)

2.38   Boult B F 1979 Concrete masonry prism testing. *Journal of the American Concrete Institute* 76: 513–35

2.39   Khalil M R A, Shrive N G, Ameny P 1987 Three-dimensional stress distribution in concrete prisms and walls. *Magazine of Concrete Research* 39(139): 73–82

2.40   Hart G C, Englekirk R E, Basharkhah A 1985 Increasing the strength and ductility in concrete masonry shear walls using confinement. In Matthys J H, Borchelt J G (eds) *Proceedings of the Third North American Masonry Conference* Arlington June 1985 pp 42.1–14

2.41   Uduehi J, Sinha B P 1988 A comparative study of prestressed beams of brickwork and concrete. In West H W H (ed) *Proceedings of the British Masonry Society* 2: 92–4

2.42   Maurenbrecher A H P 1980 The effect of test procedures on the compressive strength of masonry prisms. In Suter G T, Keller H (eds) *Proceedings of the Second Canadian Masonry Symposium* Ottawa June 1980 pp 119–32

2.43   Drysdale R G, Hamid A A 1983 Capacity of concrete block masonry under eccentric compressive loading. *Journal of the American Concrete Institute* 80: 102–8

2.44   Turkstra C J, Thomas G R 1978 Strain gradient effects in masonry. In

Noland J L, Amrhein J E (eds) *Proceedings of the North American Masonry Conference* Boulder Aug 1978, The Masonry Society, pp 22.1−21

2.45   Binda L, Baronio G 1988 Survey of brick/binder adhesion in 'powdered brick' mortars and plaster. *Masonry International* **2**(3): 87−92

2.46   Sise A, Shrive N G, Jessop E L 1988 Flexural bond strength of masonry stack prisms. In West H W H (ed) *Proceedings of the British Masonry Society* **2**: 103−7

2.47   Matthys J H 1989 Brick masonry flexural bond strengths using conventional masonry mortars. In Anderson D L (ed) *Proceedings of the Fifth Canadian Masonry Symposium* Vancouver June 1989 **2**: 745−56

2.48   Sarker A, Brown R H 1987 *Flexural Strength of Brick Masonry using the Bond Wrench* Brick Institute of America Research Report 20, 14pp

2.49   Mann W, Müller H 1982 Failure of shear-stressed masonry — an enlarged theory, tests and application to shear walls. In West H W H (ed) *Proceedings of the British Ceramic Society* **30**: 223−35

2.50   Ganz H R 1989 Failure criteria for masonry. In Anderson D L (ed) *Proceedings of the Fifth Canadian Masonry Symposium* Vancouver June 1989 **1**: 65−77

2.51   Page A W 1989 A parametric study of the behaviour of masonry shear walls. In Anderson D L (ed) *Proceedings of the Fifth Canadian Masonry Symposium* Vancouver June 1989 **1**: 341−52

2.52   Drysdale R G 1989 Building science issues for masonry construction: requirements for moisture, air and thermal barriers. In Anderson D L (ed) *Proceedings of the Fifth Canadian Masonry Symposium* Vancouver June 1989 **1**: 1−20

2.53   Grimm T C 1985 Durability of brick masonry: a review of the literature. In Grogan J C, Conway J T (eds) *Masonry: Research, Applications and Problems* American Society for Testing and Materials ASTM STP 871 pp 202−34

2.54   From: In Brief 1988. In *Construction Today* Institution of Civil Engineers, Thomas Telford Ltd Dec 1988 p 5

2.55   Hanlon J R G 1970 Prestressed concrete masonry. *Concrete* **4**(9): 356−8

2.56   Foster D 1970 Design and construction of a prestressed brickwork water tank. In West H W H, Speed K H (eds) *Proceedings of the Second International Brick Masonry Conference* Stoke-on-Trent April 1970 pp 287−94

2.57   Ganz H R 1989 New post-tensioning system for masonry. In Anderson D L (ed) *Proceedings of the Fifth Canadian Masonry Symposium* Vancouver June 1989 **1**: 165−76

3 Reinforced Masonry Elements in Flexure

A W Hendry, Professor Emeritus of Civil
Engineering,
University of Edinburgh

General

Flexural elements in masonry may be beams subjected to in-plane loading
or wall panels under lateral loading. The introduction of reinforcement
requires the use of hollow or specially shaped units or the formation of
pockets or cavities in the masonry, as indicated in Figs 3.1(a) and (b).
In these cases the reinforcing bars are embedded in concrete which may
be of the small aggregate type, often referred to as grout. There is also
the possibility of placing the reinforcement in mortar as in Fig. 3.1(c):
vertical reinforcement may be accommodated in the collar joint and
horizontal reinforcement in the bed joints. In the latter case, only rather
small diameter bars can be used and there may be difficulty in ensuring
adequate cover against moisture penetration from the faces of the
masonry. The provision of shear reinforcement may present difficulties
and may be limited to vertical bars except in the case of grouted cavity
construction.

From these considerations it will be seen that the design of reinforced
masonry beams must include the selection of units and design of the
masonry bond.

Basis of Design

A large number of investigations of the behaviour of reinforced masonry
flexural elements have confirmed that this is essentially the same as the
corresponding reinforced concrete element. Thus calculations relating
to serviceability such as deflection and cracking may be based on linear
elasticity while those relating to the ultimate limit state will require
assumptions as to the stress–strain relationship up to the failure load.

Stress–strain relationships have been referred to in Chapter 2. As
indicated there, this varies with the type of material but it is generally
accepted that a second-degree parabola provides a sufficiently accurate
representation of the stress–strain curve for both brick and block

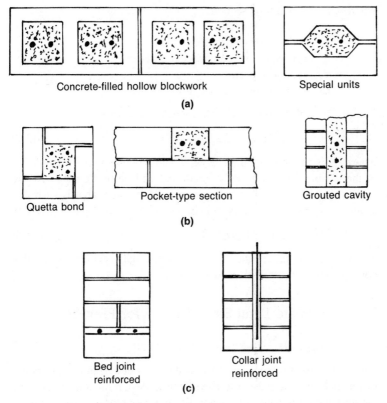

Fig. 3.1 Methods
of constructing
reinforced
masonry beams:
(a) reinforcement
in hollow or
specially shaped
units; (b)
reinforcement in
pockets or cavities
between units; (c)
reinforcement in
motor joints

Concrete-filled hollow blockwork   Special units

(a)

Quetta bond   Pocket-type section   Grouted cavity

(b)

Bed joint
reinforced   Collar joint
reinforced

(c)

masonry. There is, however, some variation in the value of the strain
at maximum stress and in the ratio of this strain to the strain at failure
of the material. It is therefore necessary to adopt representative values
of these quantities for design purposes.

In both linear elastic and ultimate load theories, it is assumed — and
confirmed experimentally — that plane sections remain plane after
bending, that is that there is linear distribution of strain across the section.
This, of course, will only hold for beams having a span to depth ratio
of about 3 or more and will not apply to deep beams which require special
consideration.

Linear Elastic Theory

The moment of resistance of a rectangular section on the basis of linear
elastic theory is given by the following equation:

$$M = 1/2 \; bxf_m \; (d-x/3) = A_s \, f_s \, (d-x/3)$$ [3.1]

where b = width of section;
          d = effective depth;
          x = depth of neutral axis;
          f_m = permissible compressive stress;
          A_s = area of steel;
          f_m = permissible tensile stress in steel.

The depth of the neutral axis can be calculated from

$$bx^2 + 2\alpha_e xA_s - 2\alpha_e dA_s = 0 \qquad [3.2]$$

where α_e is the modular ratio E_s/E_m. The modular ratio is a function of the masonry compressive strength and will lie in the range 10–40 for strong to moderately weak masonry. If the steel area is such that f_m and f_s are reached simultaneously the neutral axis depth is given by

$$x/d = 1/\{1 + (f_s/\alpha_e f_m)\}. \qquad [3.3]$$

To avoid brittle failure the steel ratio will usually be kept below that corresponding to the 'balanced section'.

Ultimate Limit State Theory for Flexure

Parabolic Stress–strain Relation

Although linear theory is still used as the basis of design in some codes of practice, it is now usual to base flexural design on consideration of the ultimate limit state using a non-linear stress block. As the strain is assumed to vary linearly from the neutral axis of the section, the variation of stress from that level to the surface of the beam will mirror the stress–strain relationship for the material. If this is assumed to be represented by the second-degree parabola

$$f = f_m\{2\epsilon/\epsilon_m - (\epsilon/\epsilon_m)^2\} \qquad [3.4]$$

as shown in Fig. 3.2, the stress block is characterized by three parameters k_1, k_2 and k_3. The latter two constants are given by the equations

$$k_2 = (4 - \epsilon_u/\epsilon_m)(12 - 4\epsilon_u/\epsilon_m)$$

$$k_3 = \{2\epsilon_u/\epsilon_m - (\epsilon_u/\epsilon_m)^2\}.$$

The constant k_1 represents the ratio of the mean to the maximum ordinate of the stress–strain curve.

It is possible to express the moment of resistance of a rectangular section in terms of these constants by equating compressive and tensile forces and taking moments about the centroid of the compression area. This gives

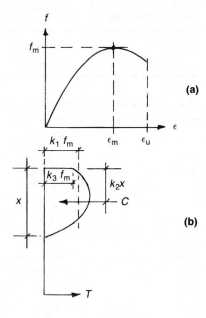

Fig. 3.2 Parabolic stress block: (a) stress–strain relationship; (b) stress block

$$M/bd^2 = \rho f_y \left[1 - \frac{\rho_v f_y \, 3k_2}{f_m\{1+k_3+\sqrt{(1-k_3)}\}} \right] \tag{3.5}$$

where b, d = breadth and effective depth of the section
                    respectively;
        ρ = steel ratio;
        f_y = yield stress of steel.

If the compressive strength of the masonry and the tensile strength of the steel are reached simultaneously, the corresponding strains are ϵ_u and ϵ_y. The moment of resistance for this condition is

$$M/bd^2 = f_m \left\{ \frac{1+k_3+\sqrt{(1-k_3)}}{3} \right\} \frac{x}{d} \left(1 - k_2 \frac{x}{d} \right) \tag{3.6}$$

where

$$\frac{x}{d} = \frac{\epsilon_u}{\epsilon_u + \epsilon_y}. \tag{3.7}$$

Equations 3.5 and 3.6 may be written in the form

$$M/bd^2 = \rho f_y \, (1 - J_1 \, \rho f_y/f_m) \tag{3.8}$$

$$M/bd^2 = f_m \, J_2. \tag{3.9}$$

For design purposes it is necessary to adopt appropriate values of the

Table 3.1 Ratio x/d

$f_y(\text{N mm}^{-2})$	460	425	250
x/d	0.449	0.461	0.515

Table 3.2 Constants for parabolic stress block

	ϵ_u/ϵ_m		
	1.0	1.5	1.75
k_2	0.375	0.417	0.450
k_3	1.000	0.750	0.437
J_1	0.562	0.556	0.617
f_y (N mm^{-2})	J_2		
465	0.249	0.274	0.261
425	0.254	0.279	0.266
250	0.277	0.303	0.288

strains ϵ_u and ϵ_y. Experiment shows that the ultimate strain for masonry beams is of the order of 0.0025−0.0035 and the latter value is often used in design codes. The yield strain for steel varies with the type of steel and on the basis of an elastic−plastic type of stress−strain diagram may be taken as the yield stress divided by Young's modulus. These assumptions result in the ratios x/d shown in Table 3.1.

Values of the constants k_2, k_3, J_1 and J_2 are then as in Table 3.2 for ϵ_u/ϵ_m equal to 1.0, 1.5 and 1.75 and for typical steel yield stresses.

From the above, the equations for the moment of resistance of a rectangular reinforced masonry beam can be written down for selected values of ϵ_u/ϵ_m and f_y. As the limiting criterion of failure is taken as the yield point of the steel (i.e. an under-reinforced section), the moment of resistance should not be greater than that given by Eq. 3.9, and, as will be shown, may be limited by shear strength.

Rectangular Stress Block

Although a parabolic stress block presents few difficulties, codes of practice frequently adopt a rectangular equivalent. This may be achieved by replacing the parabola by a rectangle of the same area, as indicated in Fig. 3.3, either by taking the mean compressive stress by the maximum strain (case A) or by taking the mean strain by the maximum stress (case B). The constant k_1 for case A is given by

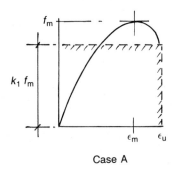

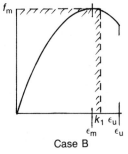

Case A

Case B

Fig. 3.3
Rectangular stress
blocks

Table 3.3 Constants for rectangular stress block

	J_1	J_2
Case A	0.667–0.750	0.250–0.281
Case B	0.500	0.290–0.347

$$k_1 = (\epsilon_u/\epsilon_m) - (\epsilon_u/\epsilon_m)^2/3. \qquad [3.10]$$

The values of J_1 and J_2 in Eqs 3.8 and 3.9 for the rectangular stress blocks shown in Fig. 3.3 are readily derived[3.1] and are indicated in Table 3.3. There is only one value of J_1 for case B since k_1 is not required for the determination of the area of the block and x/d is assumed constant.

Design Flexural Strength of Rectangular Beams

In the British Code of Practice BS 5628:Part 2,[3.2] a rectangular stress block corresponding to case B has been adopted with $J_1 = 0.5$. An arbitrary value of J_2 of 0.4 is used which is somewhat higher than the theoretical figure for a balanced section but is, on the basis of experimental results, sufficient to avoid compressive failures. For design purposes also, partial safety factors on the masonry and on the steel are introduced in Eq. 3.8 and on the masonry in Eq. 3.9. These equations thus become

$$M/bd^2 = \frac{\rho f_y}{\gamma_{ms}}\left(1 - \frac{0.5\,\rho f_y}{f_m}\frac{\gamma_{mm}}{\gamma_{ms}}\right) \le \frac{0.4\,f_m}{\gamma_{mm}}. \qquad [3.11]$$

By way of illustration Fig. 3.4 shows a family of design curves for partial safety factors of $\gamma_{ms} = 1.15$ for steel and $\gamma_{mm} = 2.0$ for masonry. The curves are plotted for steel ratios of 0.002–0.012 and for a yield stress of 460 N mm^{-2}. The cut-off for compressive failure appears as a diagonal line through the origin. A further limit on flexural failure arises

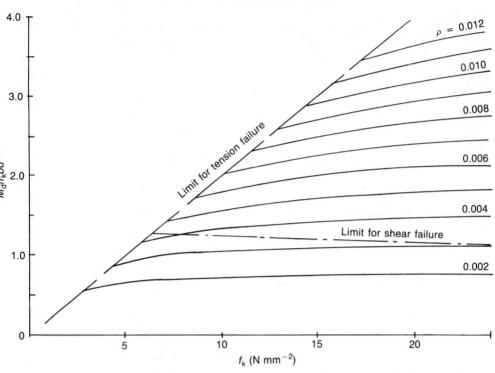

$M_d/f_k bd^2$

f_k (N mm^{-2})

$\rho = 0.012$

0.010

0.008

0.006

0.004

0.002

Limit for tension failure

Limit for shear failure

Fig. 3.4 Design curves for rectangular section reinforced masonry beams showing limits for tension and shear failure. Drawn for $f_y = 460$ N mm^{-2}, $\gamma_{ms} = 1.15$, $\gamma_{mm} = 2.0$, $\gamma_{mv} = 2.0$. Shear strength as in Eq. 3.12

from the shear strength of masonry which will be discussed in a subsequent section.

Test Results for Masonry Beams in Flexure

A considerable number of tests on reinforced masonry beams have been reported[3.1–3.15] and a comparison between some of the results and Eq. 3.8 with $J_1 = 0.5$ is shown in Fig. 3.5. Detailed examination of these results showed that all but five of those for which $M/bd^2 f_m$ was greater than 0.47 failed in compression and all but four of those for which this parameter was less than 0.32 failed in tension. Between these limits there were 32 results of which 17 failed in tension, 10 in shear and 5 in compression. There is therefore a transition zone between tension and compression failures above which Eq. 3.8 does not apply. Below this, however, the equation is in good agreement with test results both for brickwork and blockwork beams.

Within the practical design range, since the parameters on both axes of Fig. 3.5 have f_m as a divisor, there is an almost linear relationship between M/bd^2 and ρf_y. The masonry strength thus has a relatively small influence on the flexural strength of a beam; this is also evident from Fig. 3.4.

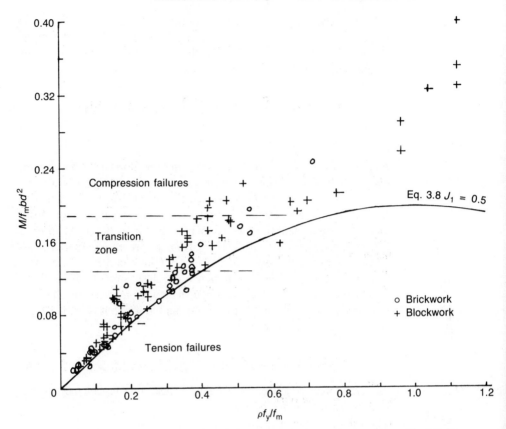

Fig. 3.5 Test results for masonry beams compared with Eq. 3.8 with $J_1 = 0.5$: (o) brickwork; (+) blockwork

Flexural Strength of Non-rectangular Sections

Various forms of flanged beam sections are used in masonry construction, for example 'T' or 'pocket' sections for retaining walls. The general principles underlying their design will be the same as for rectangular beams but certain assumptions will have to be made regarding the effective width of the flange. In reinforced concrete practice (as in BS 8110) the effective flange width of a 'T'-beam is taken as the width of the rib plus 0.2 times the distance between points of zero moment along the span. The British masonry code suggests taking the width of the rib plus 12 times the thickness of the flange but not greater than either the spacing of the ribs or one-third the height of the wall in the case of a retaining wall.

Having defined the section, the moment of resistance may be calculated by Eq. 3.8 with the proviso that M should not exceed the steel or masonry force multiplied by the lever arm assumed to be $(d - 0.5t_f)$ where t_f is the thickness of the flange.

Pocket-type walls may be treated in the same way as 'T'-sections in respect of effective width and as rectangular sections in calculating the moment of resistance provided that the neutral axis depth is not taken greater than 0.5 times the effective depth.

The Shear Strength of Masonry Beams

General

As previously observed, the shear strength of reinforced masonry beams may be a limiting factor in design and there are likely to be greater limitations in incorporating shear reinforcement than is the case with reinforced concrete beams. Although several investigations have shown that the general pattern of behaviour is similar to that of reinforced concrete, there are differences arising from the presence of mortar joints between units which are potential planes of failure in shear. Differences in form of construction also influence the shear strength of beams of similar section. Thus one can distinguish between masonry in which the reinforcement is surrounded by mortar, and in which it is embedded in concrete, as indicated in Fig. 3.1.

Shear Transmission in Reinforced Masonry Beams

As in reinforced concrete, there are three shear transmission mechanisms in reinforced masonry beams:

(a) compression zone transmission;
(b) aggregate interlock;
(c) dowel effect.

The relative importance of these three effects in grouted cavity beams has been investigated,[3.10] typical results being shown in Fig. 3.6. The contribution of each mechanism at a section of the beam was calculated from strain measurements by formulae originally developed for reinforced concrete. In this example, compression zone transmission accounted for some 40 per cent of the shear force, with aggregate interlock and dowel effect contributing smaller proportions. Grouted cavity and filled hollow blockwork of 'U'-cross-section will most closely approach the strength of reinforced concrete, whereas in brickwork sections aggregate interlock will be more or less absent and dowel effect will be limited owing to the weakness of the bond strength of the lowermost course of bricks on which it depends. Figure 3.7 shows a comparison between the strength of reinforced concrete, grouted cavity and brickwork beams of the same dimensions[3.9] to illustrate these points.

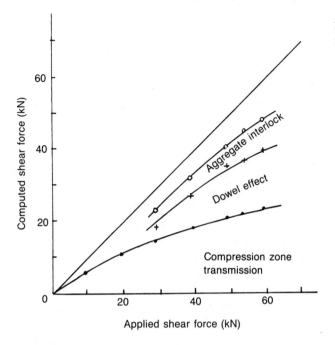

Fig. 3.6 Shear
transmission
mechanisms

Beams with Reinforcement Embedded in Concrete

A large number of tests have been carried out to investigate the strength
of grouted cavity beams,[3.9–3.11] beams built in concrete-filled hollow
blockwork[3.12–3.15] and pocket-type sections, in all of which the
reinforcement is embedded in concrete.

As previously observed, the behaviour of grouted cavity beams is
intermediate between that of reinforced concrete and brickwork beams
of the same section (cf. Fig. 3.7), their strength as between the two being
in proportion to the width of the concrete core. The effect of the shear
span ratio is appreciable in this type of beam, as may be seen from Fig.
3.7. The increase in strength as the shear span ratio is decreased is
attributed to the development of a tied arch effect within the beam, an
effect well known in reinforced concrete beams.[3.16] The shear strength
of masonry beams is also influenced by the steel ratio but only to a minor
extent by the masonry strength.[3.17]

The characteristics of beams built in concrete-filled hollow blockwork
is generally similar to that of reinforced concrete beams, and are indicated
in Fig. 3.8. The shear strength of pocket-type sections has also been
examined[3.18] and would appear to be of the same order as that of the

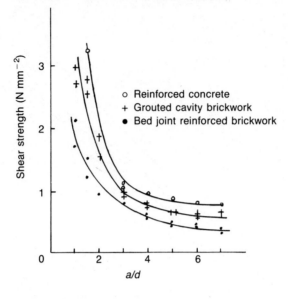

Fig. 3.7 Shear
strength of
reinforced
concrete and
reinforced
brickwork beams

o Reinforced concrete
+ Grouted cavity brickwork
• Bed joint reinforced brickwork

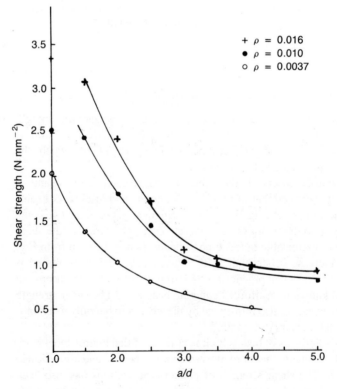

Fig. 3.8 Shear
strength of
reinforced,
concrete-filled
hollow blockwork
beams

+ $\rho = 0.016$
• $\rho = 0.010$
o $\rho = 0.0037$

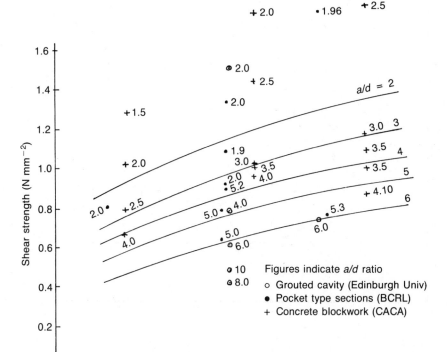

Fig. 3.9 Effect of steel ratio and shear span ratio on shear strength of reinforced masonry beams

other forms of construction in which the reinforcement is embedded in concrete.

The combined effect of steel ratio and shear span ratio is illustrated in Fig. 3.9 in which the shear strength of a wide range of beams is plotted against the percentage reinforcement. The shear span ratio is indicated against each point and approximate curves have been drawn corresponding to shear span ratios from 2.0–6.0. These relationships are reflected in the formula for shear strength given in BS 5628:Part 2:

$$(0.35+17.5\rho) \; [2.5-0.25a/d] \; \not> \; 1.75 \text{ N mm}^{-2}. \qquad [3.12]$$

The quantity within the first brackets represents the shear strength for shear span ratios greater than 6. Below this ratio the shear strength is enhanced by the multiplier within the square brackets up to a maximum of 1.75 N mm^{-2}.

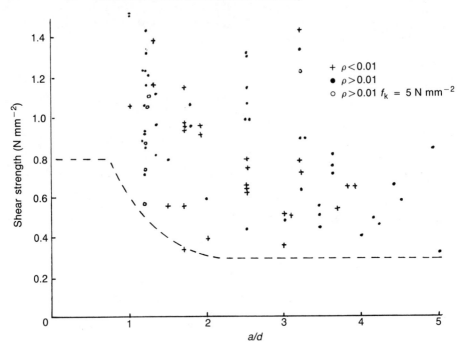

Fig. 3.10 Shear
strength of
reinforced
brickwork beams

Brick Masonry Beams

In this type of beam the reinforcement is embedded in mortar, either
in the bed joints or in the collar joint of the brickwork. In such beams,
aggregate interlock and dowel effect, as noted above, will both be
relatively small and their strength for given dimensions and reinforcement
ratio will be less than for those in which the steel is surrounded with
concrete. The extent of this is indicated in Fig. 3.7.

A considerable number of test results have been reported for the shear
strength of brickwork beams and are summarized in Fig. 3.10.
Examination of these results shows that there is no significant increase
in strength with increase in the steel ratio but there is an increase with
decreasing a/d ratio. The results are characterized by a very large scatter
and it would appear that a lower bound shear strength of 0.35 N mm^{-2}
would be appropriate with an increase when the shear span ratio is less
than 2. Thus for 1:0.25:3 and 1:0.5:4.5 mortars BS 5628:Part 2 allows
the shear strength of 0.35 N mm^{-2} to be increased by a factor of $2d/a$
when the shear span ratio is less than this limit but not to exceed
0.7 N mm^{-2}.

Shear Strength Limitation on Flexural Design of Masonry Beams

Figure 3.5 shows a family of design curves from which the moment of resistance of a section can be determined, given its dimensions and the steel ratio, on the basis of flexural failure in tension. In many cases, however, the flexural strength will not be attained owing to the limit of shear strength being reached first. This condition can be indicated on Fig. 3.4 in the following manner. The shear stress in the beam must not exceed

$$v = V/bd \qquad\qquad [3.13]$$

where V is the shear force on the section, b the width of section and d the effective depth. Taking the shear span as

$$a_v = M_{max}/V, \qquad\qquad [3.14]$$

then the limiting condition for shear failure is

$$\frac{M_{max}}{bd^2} \not> v(a_v/d) \qquad\qquad [3.15]$$

This condition has been superimposed on the curves of Fig. 3.4 using shear strengths and partial safety factors from BS 5628. From this it will be seen that, in the absence of shear reinforcement, shear strength will be a limiting factor unless the steel ratio is less than 0.003.

Shear Reinforcement in Masonry Beams

There are certain obvious limitations in introducing shear reinforcement in masonry beams. These are least in grouted cavity construction, where both vertical and diagonal bars can be accommodated, and greatest in brick masonry. However, even in the latter type it is possible to introduce vertical bars by suitable design of the brickwork bond. Vertical bars can also be placed in concrete-filled hollow blockwork.

Following reinforced concrete practice, the shear strength with vertical bars is given by

$$f_{sv} = (f_v + A_{sv}\, f_y/bs_v) \qquad\qquad [3.16]$$

where f_v = shear strength without shear steel;
         A_{sv} = shear steel area;
         f_y = yield stress of shear steel;
         b = breadth of section;
         s_v = spacing of bars.

Comparison with the limited experimental results available shows reasonable agreement.[3.19]

Deflection and Crack Widths

Deflection of Reinforced Masonry Beams

Reinforced masonry beams typically exhibit a bilinear load−deflection curve, the transition point coinciding with the load at which the masonry cracks. Deflections up to the cracking point may be calculated on the basis of the transformed uncracked section with an appropriate value of Young's modulus. Beyond that point, the flexural rigidity must be based on the transformed cracked section. For this purpose, the neutral axis depth is given by

$$\frac{x}{d} = -\alpha_e\rho + \sqrt{(\alpha_e^2\,\rho^2 + 2\alpha_e\rho_1)} \qquad\qquad [3.17]$$

where α_e is the modular ratio and ρ is the steel ratio. For a singly reinforced beam the second moment of area of a cracked section is

$$I_{cr} = \left\{\frac{1}{3}\left(\frac{x}{d}\right)^3 + \alpha_e\rho\left(1-\frac{x}{d}\right)^2 + \alpha_e\rho\left(\frac{x}{d}\right)^2\right\}bd^3. \qquad [3.18]$$

Deflections can be calculated[3.20] from the following moment−curvature relationship:

$$\frac{1}{r} = \frac{M}{EI_u} + \frac{M-M_{cr}}{0.85\,I_c} \qquad\qquad [3.19]$$

where M = applied moment;
EI_u = flexural rigidity of transformed uncracked section;
M_{cr} = cracking moment = $I_u\,f_t/(H-x)$;
H = overall depth of section;
f_t = tensile strength of masonry;
EI_c = flexural rigidity of transformed cracked section.

Deflections in terms of $1/r$ for common loading cases are

Concentrated load at midspan $a = \dfrac{1}{r},\ l^2/12$

Uniformly distributed load $= \dfrac{1}{r},\ l^2/9.6$

Equal end moments $= \dfrac{1}{r},\ l^2/8$

The value of Young's modulus for masonry is discussed in Chapter 2.

In selecting a value for deflection calculations, due attention must be given to the duration of loading since the effective E for long-term loading is likely to be at least half of that for short-term loads.

Estimation of Crack Widths in Masonry Beams

With the safety factors and detailing rules prescribed, the limit state of flexural cracking should not often be a design criterion. If, however, it is necessary to examine crack widths it is possible to use formulae originally developed for reinforced concrete, although application of the more refined of these would hardly be justified in view of the limited knowledge of crack development in reinforced masonry members. The main differences between reinforced concrete and reinforced masonry beams in this context will be, firstly, that cracks will be located at vertical joints between units and, secondly, that distances from the surface to the reinforcing bars will be greater in the latter case.

A tentative formula derived from tests on grouted cavity beams[3.20] gives the crack width as $3\,a_{cr}\,\epsilon_m$ where a_{cr} is the distance to the nearest reinforcing bar and ϵ_m the surface strain at the point where the crack width is measured. The latter is to be estimated on the basis of a cracked section and linear distribution of strain.

Bond Stress in Reinforced Masonry Beams

Bond stresses result from change in shear force along the length of a beam and at the ends of reinforcing bars. The first of these is known as local bond stress and results from the difference between the bending moments at two sections of a beam divided by the lever arm. This force is resisted by the local bond stress multiplied by the surface area of the bars between the two sections. Checking of this stress is no longer required in the British code for reinforced concrete, BS 8110, as it has been found[3.21] that, provided the anchorage length is sufficient, the local bond stress does not seem to have much significance. The same view appears to have been adopted in the masonry code, BS 5628:Part 2 which refers only to anchorage bond strength.

The anchorage bond strength is taken to be the force in the bar divided by the anchorage length × bar perimeter. At the ultimate limit state the anchorage bond stress which may be developed will depend on whether the bar is embedded in mortar or in concrete. For the former BS 5628 allows a characteristic bond stress of 1.5 N mm^{-2} for plain bars and 2.0 N mm^{-2} for deformed bars. For bars in concrete the corresponding values are 1.8 and 2.5 N mm^{-2}. In detailing reinforced masonry beams the necessary anchorage length may be developed by hooks or bends for which design codes set out appropriate rules.

Masonry Wall Beams

Considerable attention has been given to the study of composite action between masonry walls and concrete or steel beams on which they are built.[3.22] On the other hand, only limited work has been reported on beams built of masonry[3.23] the lower courses of which, with suitable reinforcement, could perform the same function as the more conventional steel or concrete beam. It would appear, however, that masonry wall beams reinforced in the lower courses may be treated in the same way as composite elements provided that an assumption is made as to the effective dimensions of the equivalent supporting beam. In the absence of specific information, this must remain a matter of judgement but a depth of about three times the thickness of the masonry would seem reasonable.

It is known that the structural action of a composite wall beam is as indicated in Fig. 3.11, vertical and shear forces between the wall and support beam being concentrated towards the ends of the beam resulting in a kind of arching action in the wall. A convenient solution for the analysis of this system is available[3.24] based on the use of a parameter

$$R_f = \sqrt[4]{\left(\frac{E_m t\, H^3}{E_s I} \right)} \qquad\qquad [3.20]$$

where E_m = Young's modulus for masonry;
t = the thickness of the wall;
H = the height of the wall;
$E_s I$ = the flexural rigidity of the beam.

This is a measure of the ratio of wall to beam stiffness. The ratio of

Fig. 3.11 Structural behaviour of reinforced masonry wall beam systems: (a) arching action in wall; (b) interface stresses between wall and beam

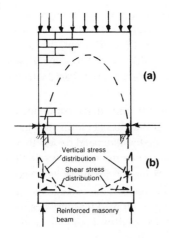

Vertical stress distribution

Shear stress distribution

(a)

(b)

Reinforced masonry beam

the maximum to the average compressive stress in the wall, derived by finite element calculations, is given by the equation

$$\frac{f_m}{(W_w/lt)} = (1+\beta R_f) \qquad [3.21]$$

where f_m = the maximum compressive stress in the wall;
W_w = the total vertical load on the beam;
l = the span;
t = the thickness of the masonry;
β = a coefficient (cf. Fig. 3.12).

Assuming a triangular distribution of stress between the wall and the beam, the contact length is thus, from Eq. 3.21,

$$l_v = \frac{l}{(1+\beta R_f)}. \qquad [3.22]$$

The horizontal force in the beam is transmitted from the wall by shear at the interface and is given by

$$T = W_w(\alpha - \gamma R_a) \qquad [3.23]$$

where $R_a = E_w t H/EA$ and α and γ are further coefficients derived by finite element analysis and having the values shown in Fig. 3.12.
Finite element analysis has shown that the shear stress acts over a length two to three times that of the vertical stress, that is

$$l_s = \frac{2l}{(1+\beta R_f)}. \qquad [3.24]$$

Again assuming a triangular stress distribution, and using Eq. 3.24, the maximum shear stress is

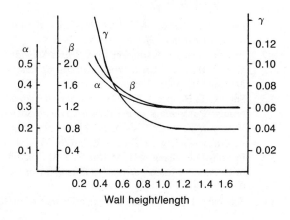

Fig. 3.12 Parameters α, β and γ for calculation of forces in wall-beam system

Table 3.4 Formulae for maximum beam bending moment

---

1. $R_f \leq 5$ — Stiff beam

$$M_m = \frac{W_w l - 10\ W_w d(\alpha - \gamma R_a)}{5(1 + \beta R_f)}$$

2. $5 < R_f < 7$ — Flexible beam

$$M_m = \frac{W_w l - 8\ W_w d(\alpha - \gamma R_a)}{5.33(1 + b R_f)}$$

3. $R \geq 7$ — Very flexible beam

$$M_m = \frac{W_w l - 6\ W_w d(\alpha - \gamma R_a)}{6(1 + \beta R_f)}$$

$$V_m = \frac{W_w(\alpha - \gamma R_a)(1 + \beta R_f)}{lt}. \qquad [3.25]$$

The bending moment at any section of the beam results from a combination of moments due to the vertical loading and the shear force at the interface of the wall and the beam. The bending moments in the beam depend on the parameters R_f and R_a. The formulae in Table 3.4 give maximum values for various ranges of R_f.

Investigations[3.25] have indicated that centrally placed openings in a wall beam have a relatively small effect on bending moments in the beam but a large opening at about quarter span will double the bending moment. It will be necessary to check the vertical compressive stress in the wall by the usual design methods.

References

3.1   Davies S R, Hendry A W 1986 Reinforced masonry beams. *Proceedings of the British Masonry Society* **1**: 73–6

3.2   British Standards Institution 1985 *British Standard Code of Practice for Use of Masonry:Part 2:Structural Use of Reinforced and Prestressed Masonry* BS 5628, London

3.3   Suter G T, Hendry A W 1975 Limit state design of reinforced brickwork beams. *Proceedings of the British Ceramic Society* **24**: 191–6

3.4   Withey M O 1933 Tests of brick masonry beams. *Proceedings of the American Society for Testing Materials* **33**: 651–65

3.5   Parsons D E, Stang A H, McBurney J W 1932 Shear tests of reinforced brick masonry beams. *Journal of Research National Bureau of Standards* **9**: 747–68

3.6   Schneider H 1976 Tests on shear resistance of masonry. *Proceedings of the Fourth International Brick Masonry Conference* Brugge 1976 4.b.12

3.7 Thomas F G, Sims L G 1939 The strength of some reinforced brick masonry beams. *Structural Engineer* **17**: 330–49

3.8 Garwood T G, Tomlinson A 1982 The design construction and test performance of reinforced brickwork beams containing tension and shear reinforcement. *Proceedings of the British Ceramic Society* **30**: 316–26

3.9 Suter G, Keller H 1976 Shear strength of grouted reinforced masonry beams. *Proceedings of the Fourth International Brick Masonry Conference* Brugge 1976 4.c.2

3.10 Osman Y A, Hendry A W 1982 An investigation into the behaviour of reinforced grouted cavity brick beams under bending and shear. *Proceedings of the British Ceramic Society* **30**: 346–54

3.11 Sinha B P 1982 Reinforced grouted cavity brickwork. *Journal of International Council for Building Research* **10**(4):226

3.12 Suter G T, Keller H 1980 *Concrete Masonry Beam Tests* Carleton University, Ottawa

3.13 Roberts J J 1980 *The Behaviour of Vertically Reinforced Concrete Blockwork Subject to Lateral Loading* Cement and Concrete Association Technical Report 506

3.14 Roberts J J 1980 *Further Work on the Behaviour of Reinforced Concrete Blockwork Subject to Lateral Loading* Cement and Concrete Association Technical Report 531

3.15 Rathbone A J 1980 *The Behaviour of Reinforced Concrete Blockwork Beams* Cement and Concrete Association Technical Report 540

3.16 Kong F K, Evans R H 1987 *Reinforced and Prestressed Concrete* 3rd edn Van Nostrand Reinhold, Wokingham p 200

3.17 Sinha B P, de Vekey R C 1982 Factors affecting the shear strength of reinforced grouted brickwork beams and slabs. *Proceedings of the Sixth International Brick Masonry Conference* Rome 1982 pp 831–42

3.18 Edgell G J, Tellet J, West H W H 1982 Research into the behaviour of pocket type retaining walls. *Proceedings of the Sixth International Brick Masonry Conference* Rome 1982 pp 805–16

3.19 Hendry A W 1983 *Structural Brickwork* Macmillan, London pp 149–53

3.20 Osman Y A A 1983 Behaviour of reinforced grouted cavity brickwork beams. PhD thesis, University of Edinburgh

3.21 Kong F K, Evans R H 1987 *Reinforced and Prestressed Concrete* 3rd edn Van Nostrand Reinhold, Wokingham p 223

3.22 Hendry A W 1990 *Structural Masonry* Macmillan, London pp 218–28

3.23 Mortelmans F, Van Biervliet L 1982 Tests on wall beams in reinforced masonry. *Proceedings of the Fifth International Brick Masonry Conference* Washington 1979 pp 314–19

3.24 Davies S R, Ahmed A E 1978 An approximate method for analysing composite wall beams. *Proceedings of the British Cermaic Society* **27**: 305–20

3.25 Davies S R, Ahmed A E 1976 Composite action of wall beams with openings. *Proceedings of the Fourth International Brick Masonry Conference* Brugge 1976 4.b.6

4 Prestressed Masonry Beams

Dr B P Sinha, University of Edinburgh

Introduction

The tensile strength of masonry, either concrete blockwork or brickwork, is very low compared to its compressive strength. Consequently, it cannot be used for flexural members, which resist the applied load, primarily in bending. This deficiency can, however, be overcome by reinforcing or prestressing. The methods of reinforcing and the theory behind it have been dealt with in Chapter 3.

Prestressing of masonry elements essentially means applying precompression, causing stresses of desired magnitude to counteract tensile stresses developed under service loading. By taking advantage of the greater compressive strength of the masonry and choosing an appropriate degree of prestress, the tensile stress can be completely eliminated during service loading.

Methods of Prestressing

The methods and techniques[4.1, 4.2] used for prestressing masonry are similar to concrete. These are pretensioning and post-tensioning.

Pretensioning

In pretensioning, the tendons or wires are tensioned against external abutments and the masonry is built with a preformed cavity around it. The cavity is filled later with grout or concrete to embed the tendons or wires within the masonry to form a monolithic construction. When the masonry and the grout or concrete have attained sufficient strength, the tendons or wires are then released slowly from the abutments thus transferring the prestressing force to the grout or concrete and eventually to the masonry by bond.

This method of prestressing is most suitable for factory production of prestressed masonry elements and has been used to manufacture the Stahlton[4.3, 4.4] ceramic flooring system.

Post-tensioning

In post-tensioning, the tendons or wires are tensioned against the masonry after it has reached sufficient strength. The tendon ends are anchored against the masonry element by special anchoring devices,[4.1] which consist of a wedge or threaded nut system. These devices transfer the prestressing force into the masonry either through external steel bearing plates or specially designed concrete end blocks.

After prestressing, the tendons or wires can be bonded with masonry by grouting or left unbonded. It is highly desirable to use bonded tendons in masonry flexural elements, since those with unbonded tendons suffer from various disadvantages, such as:

(a) lower ultimate strength;
(b) increased deformation and crack spacing associated with wider cracks; and
(c) tendons need special protection from corrosion.

In addition, if the grouting ensures proper bonding and reaches sufficient strength, the wedges, barrel and end plates may be removed from the beam without any loss of strength[4.5] making it cheaper than elements with unbonded tendons. Initially, a masonry beam in such a situation acts both as pretensioning abutment and post-tensioned load-carrying element and later as a pretensioned element without wedges, barrel or end plates.

Post-tensioning, as a method, is easier and allows prestressing at site, and hence is most likely to be used in practice for masonry. Post-tensioned hollow concrete block[4.3] beams (20 m span) with ungrouted wires were used as early as 1942 for a roof at Tournai, Belgium.

Advantages of Prestressed Masonry

Prestressed masonry offers several advantages over reinforced masonry.

Efficient Use of Materials

In a reinforced masonry flexural element, only the masonry on the compression region above or below the neutral axis, as the case may be, contributes to the load-carrying capacity. Although the rest of the masonry on the tensile region provides for the composite action, it really makes no contribution to the load-carrying capacity — thus much of the material is wasted, or at least used inefficiently. By contrast, in prestressed masonry flexural elements, the whole section being in compression remains effective in resisting the applied service loading. Thus it results in the efficient use of the material. Besides, the cracks in reinforced masonry usually develop at a relatively small fraction of the service load and to keep these cracks within acceptable limits the steel strain has to be kept low. Therefore, high-tensile steel cannot be used to its optimum in reinforced masonry.

Enhanced Shear Resistance

At service loads, the shear resistance of prestressed masonry beams is enhanced compared to that of reinforced masonry. In an uncracked section, the diagonal tensile stress at the centroid is reduced by prestress, which results in this enhancement. Figure 4.1 shows the relationship between the shear strength of prestressed and reinforced brickwork beams with shear span and effective depth ratio. It is very clear from Fig. 4.1 that the ultimate shear strength[4.6–4.8] of prestressed brickwork beams is much higher than reinforced brickwork.

Higher Fatigue Strength

In prestressed masonry beams, the amplitude of stress variation in the steel from zero to working load is much less than in a comparable reinforced beam. Therefore its resistance to fatigue under cyclic loading is much greater.

Fig. 4.1 Shear strength of reinforced,[4.14] partially prestressed[4.8] and fully prestressed[4.6,4.7] brickwork beams

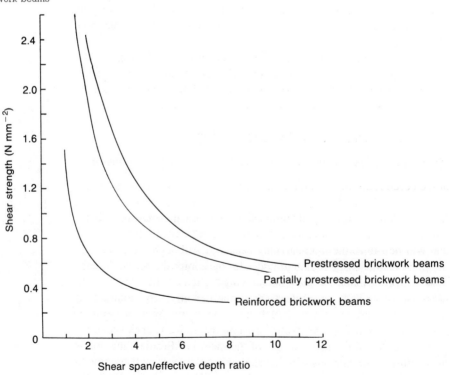

Improved Performance at or above Service Load

In prestressed elements, the flexural deflection due to prestress usually acts in the opposite direction to that caused by the service loading. Hence, by choosing an appropriate degree of prestress, the deflection and cracking under service loading can be completely eliminated from prestressed masonry flexural elements. In addition, a prestressed masonry flexural member will not suffer from ill effects of overloading since the cracks[4.5] developed due to overloading will close completely on its removal. Likewise, there will be complete or substantial recovery from the additional deflection[4.5] suffered due to overloading.

The construction of post-tensioned brickwork is generally easier than reinforced brickwork and only requires greater supervision during the post-tensioning operation.

Basic Theory

The elastic theory of combined bending and direct stresses is used for the design and analysis of prestressed masonry flexural elements. The criteria used in the design of such elements are the allowable stresses in compression and tension at transfer and at service loads. It is ensured that the stresses developed at the extreme top and bottom fibres of a flexural member during prestressing and at service loads should be less than or equal to the allowable tensile and compressive stresses for the masonry. In addition, the designer must be satisfied that the member possesses an adequate margin of safety against the ultimate strength in flexure and shear.

Fig. 4.2 Cross-section of beam and stress distribution at transfer and in service: (a) beam cross-section; (b) stress due to prestress; (c) stress due to self-weight; (d) combined stress at transfer; (e) stress due to effective prestress; (f) stress due to service load including the self-weight; (g) combined stress due to effective prestress and the service load

Stresses at Transfer and in Service

Consider the cross-section (Fig. 4.2) of a simply supported and uniformly loaded masonry beam in which the initial prestressing force P is applied at the eccentricity of e_s. Initially the section in Fig. 4.2(a) is subjected to an axial load and hogging moment due to the application of the prestress at an eccentricity of e_s. The stress distribution is shown in Fig. 4.2(b). During the application of prestress, the beam will start lifting upward and will be subjected to a sagging moment M_i due to the self-weight,

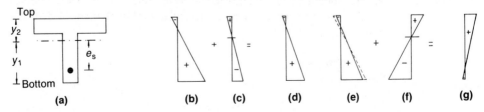

(a)   (b)   (c)   (d)   (e)   (f)   (g)

together with any dead weight acting on the beam at that moment. The stress distribution due to moment M_i is shown in Fig. 4.2(c) and the combined stress due to the initial prestress P and the sagging moment M_i is represented in Fig. 4.2(d). At the critical section, the tensile stress at the top and the compressive stress at the bottom should be less than or equal to the allowable stresses for the masonry at transfer. Generally, the combined stress distribution (Fig. 4.2(d)) and the design constraints following the theory described by Allen[4.1] can be represented by Eqs 4.1 and 4.2 in the following section.

At Initial Transfer

Stress at top:

$$f_{2i} = \frac{P}{A} - \frac{Pe_sy_2}{I} + \frac{M_i}{Z_2} \geq f_{tt} \qquad [4.1]$$

$$= \frac{P}{A} - \frac{Pe_s}{Z_2} + \frac{M_i}{Z_2} \geq f_{tt}.$$

Stress at bottom:

$$f_{1i} = \frac{P}{A} + \frac{Pe_sy_1}{I} - \frac{M_i}{Z_1} \leq f_{ct} \qquad [4.2]$$

$$= \frac{P}{A} + \frac{Pe_s}{Z_1} - \frac{M_i}{Z_1} \leq f_{ct}.$$

The initial prestress P will be reduced due to various losses as described in the Loss of Prestress section (p.93). Let α be the loss ratio, hence

$$P_e = \alpha P \qquad [4.3]$$

where P_e is the effective prestress during service.

The stress distribution due to the effective prestress is given in Fig. 4.2(e); the stresses will be less than those shown in Fig. 4.2(b), because of prestress loss. The stresses due to service loading are shown in Fig. 4.2(f) and the combined stress distribution due to the effective prestress and the service load is given in Fig. 4.2(g). In general, the controlling conditions for the design will be that the compressive stress at the top and the tensile stress at the bottom (Fig. 4.2(g)) in service at the critical section should be less than or equal to the relevant allowable stresses in the masonry. This can be represented by Eqs 4.4 and 4.5 in the following section.

At Service

Stress at top:

$$f_{2s} = \alpha \left(\frac{P}{A} - \frac{Pe_s}{Z_2} \right) + \frac{M_s}{Z_2} \leq f_{cs}. \qquad [4.4]$$

Stress at bottom:

$$f_{1s} = \alpha\left(\frac{P}{A} + \frac{Pe_s}{Z_1}\right) - \frac{M_s}{Z_2} \geq f_{ts}.$$ [4.5]

By eliminating P and e_s from Eqs 4.1, 4.2, 4.4 and 4.5, the values of Z_2 and Z_1 are obtained as

$$Z_2 \geq \frac{M_s - \alpha M_i}{f_{cs} - \alpha f_{tt}}$$ [4.6]

$$Z_1 \geq \frac{M_s - \alpha M_i}{\alpha f_{ct} - \alpha f_{ts}}.$$ [4.7]

Critical Sections

At the critical sections, the condition of Eqs 4.6 and 4.7 must be satisfied. The critical sections are subjected to the most unfavourable combination of loading and prestress either at transfer or in service or both. In a simply supported post-tensioned masonry beam with curved tendon profile, the bending moment will be maximum at mid-span, both at transfer and in service.

Now, let us assume that the bending moment at mid-span of the beam is M_s which consists of the moment due to the live and dead weight, M_{d+L} and M_i due to the self-weight, hence

$$M_s = M_{d+L} + M_i.$$ [4.8]

Substituting the value of M_s from Eq. 4.8 in Eqs 4.6 and 4.7, the values of Z_2 and Z_1 become

$$Z_2 \geq \frac{M_{d+L} + M_i(1 - \alpha)}{f_{cs} - \alpha f_{tt}}$$ [4.9]

$$Z_1 \geq \frac{M_{d+L} + M_i(1 - \alpha)}{\alpha f_{ct} - f_{ts}}.$$ [4.10]

Unless special clay units are manufactured to suit the profile, the use of a curved tendon will be limited to post-tensioned, grouted cavity construction in brickwork or hollow concrete blocks, both of which require appreciable amounts of infill concrete. This would to a great extent negate the advantage of using masonry beams.

In the case of a pretensioned or post-tensioned fully bonded masonry beam with straight tendons, the critical stress condition exists near the supports at transfer. Near supports of the beam, the moment M_i may be assumed to be zero. Thus, substituting the value of M_i in Eqs 4.6 and 4.7 and using Eq. 4.8, the values of Z_2 and Z_1 are given by

$$Z_2 \geq \frac{M_{d+L} + M_i}{f_{cs} - \alpha f_{tt}} \qquad [4.11]$$

$$Z_1 \geq \frac{M_{d+L} + M_i}{\alpha f_{ct} - f_{ts}}. \qquad [4.12]$$

As can be seen from Eqs 4.9–4.12, the values of Z_2 and Z_1 not only depend on the chosen tendon profiles but also on the unknown mid-span moment M_i due to the self-weight. Initially, the value of the moment M_i is assumed[4.9] as a percentage of the mid-span moment M_s and Z_2 and Z_1 are found from Eqs 4.9–4.12 for the particular tendon profile. In addition, the cross-section chosen must conform to the sizes of masonry units. A subsequent check is made to verify that the assumed value of M_i corresponds to the cross-section chosen, otherwise the value is modified.

Once the suitable cross-section has been found, the prestressing force and its eccentricity can be obtained from the conditions that the tensile stresses do not exceed the allowable limit. Hence, using Eqs 4.1 and 4.5 the values of P_{min} and e_{max} are

$$P_{min} = \frac{A\{(M_s - \alpha M_i) + (Z_1 f_{ts} + \alpha Z_2 f_{tt})\}}{\alpha(Z_1 + Z_2)} \qquad [4.13]$$

$$e_{max} = \frac{Z_2}{A} + \frac{M_i - Z_2 f_{tt}}{P}. \qquad [4.14]$$

Permissible Tendon Zone

From Eq. 4.14, it can be seen that the bending moment and prestressing force also have an influence on the eccentricity at any particular section. In a simply supported beam, the bending moment varies from zero at supports to maximum at the centre, whereas the value of P is assumed constant. In the post-tensioned beam with curved tendon profile, the horizontal component of the prestress, $P \cos \theta$ at any section is taken virtually equal to P, as the angle θ will be small.

Since the eccentricity e_{max} has been calculated at the critical section subjected to the maximum bending moment, it is imperative to reduce it at various sections of the beam taking into account the reduction in the bending moment to keep the tensile stress within the allowable limit. As the tensile stresses become the limiting criteria, using Eqs 4.1 and 4.4 the lower and upper limits of the tendon zone can be established as

$$e_1 (\text{lower limit}) \leq \frac{Z_2}{A} + \frac{M_i - Z_2 f_{tt}}{P} \qquad [4.15]$$

$$e_2 (\text{upper limit}) \leq -\frac{Z_1}{A} + \frac{M_s + Z_1 f_{ts}}{\alpha P}. \qquad [4.16]$$

Beams in which Tensile Strength of Masonry is Ignored

So far the theory described in this section is of a general nature. Usually, the tensile strength of masonry is ignored in practice. At present, it is convenient to build pre- or post-tensioned masonry beams with fully bonded straight tendons. In such cases the section moduli can be obtained from Eqs 4.11 and 4.12 by ignoring f_{tt} and f_{ts}, the tensile strengths both at transfer and service. Since the bending moment M_i at the critical section near the end is zero, the lower limit of the eccentricity from Eq. 4.15 becomes

$$e_1 \leq \frac{Z_2}{A} \quad \text{where} \quad \frac{Z_2}{A} \text{ is the 'kern' limit.} \qquad [4.17]$$

(*Note*: for a rectangular section, $Z_2/A = d/6$.)

This eccentricity will, then, govern the value of the prestressing force. From Eqs 4.1 and 4.4 or 4.13, the value of the prestressing force P can be obtained as

$$P = \frac{M_s A}{\alpha(Z_1 + Z_2)}$$

$$= \frac{3M_s}{\alpha d} \quad \text{(for a rectangular section).} \qquad [4.18]$$

Ultimate Strength of Prestressed Masonry Beams in Flexure

After cracking and approaching failure, the behaviour of prestressed masonry beams is akin to reinforced masonry. Hence a similar method of analysis can be applied, with some modification, to find the ultimate flexural strength of prestressed masonry. For all practical purposes, the final flexural failure is assumed to happen by crushing of the masonry at an ultimate compressive strain, ϵ_{mu} (Fig. 4.3). Near failure the stress distribution diagram for the compression zone will correspond to the actual stress–strain relationship of the masonry and can be defined by two parameters, namely the average compressive stress $k_1 f_m$ and the distance of the centre of compression, $k_2 d_c$ from the extreme compression fibre.

These conditions at flexural failure of a prestressed rectangular masonry beam are shown in Fig. 4.3. Referring to Fig. 4.3(c), for equilibrium

$$k_1 f_m b d_c = A_{ps} f_{pb}$$

or

$$d_c = \frac{A_{ps} f_{pb}}{k_1 f_m b}. \qquad [4.19]$$

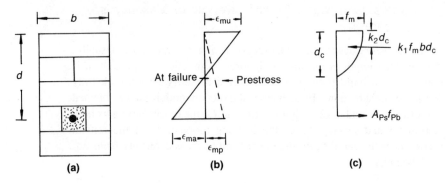

Fig. 4.3 (a) Cross-section of beam; (b) strain distributon; (c) forces at failure

At failure, the tendon strain ϵ_{pb} consists of (i) ϵ_{pa} due to the applied load and (ii) ϵ_{pe} due to the effective prestress, hence

$$\epsilon_{pb} = \epsilon_{pa} + \epsilon_{pe}. \qquad [4.20]$$

Referring to Fig. 4.3(b) and assuming that full bond exists between brickwork, grout and steel at failure, the value of ϵ_{pa} is given by

$$\epsilon_{pa} = \epsilon_{ma} + \epsilon_{mp} \qquad [4.21]$$

where

$$\epsilon_{mp} = \frac{\text{Prestressing stress in masonry at tendon level}}{E_m}.$$

In the case of an unbonded tendon, the strain in steel will be less and Eq. 4.21 can be modified to

$$\epsilon_{pa} = \beta_2 \epsilon_{ma} + \beta_1 \epsilon_{mp} \qquad [4.22]$$

where β_1 and β_2 are the bond factors. Typical values associated with concrete[4.2] are $\beta_1 = 0.5$ and β_2 between 0.1 and 0.25. Referring to Fig. 4.3(b) and for a fully bonded beam,

$$\epsilon_{pa} = \epsilon_{mu}\left(\frac{d-d_c}{d_c}\right) + \epsilon_{mp}. \qquad [4.23]$$

Substituting the value of ϵ_{pa} in Eq. 4.20

$$\epsilon_{pb} = \epsilon_{mu}\left(\frac{d-d_c}{d_c}\right) + \epsilon_{mp} + \epsilon_{pe}$$

or

$$d_c = \frac{\epsilon_{mu}}{\epsilon_{pb} + \epsilon_{mu} - \epsilon_{mp} - \epsilon_{pe}}\, d. \qquad [4.24]$$

Substituting the value of d_c from Eq. 4.19 in Eq. 4.24 and rearranging,

$$f_{pb} = \frac{k_1 f_m b d}{A_{ps}} \frac{\epsilon_{mu}}{\epsilon_{pb} + \epsilon_{mu} - \epsilon_{mp} - \epsilon_{pe}}. \qquad [4.25]$$

At failure, the values of two unknowns f_{pb} and ϵ_{pb} must satisfy Eq. 4.25 and also the stress–strain curve of the steel given in relevant standards. Once the values of f_{pb} and ϵ_{pb} are known, the depth of the neutral axis d_c can be obtained from Eqs 4.19 or 4.24.

The ultimate moment can be obtained by taking the moment of the tensile force about the centre of compression, as

$$M_u = A_{ps} f_{pb} (d - k_2 d_c). \qquad [4.26]$$

The equations derived in this section are of a general nature and can be modified to suit other types of stress block, as for example, in BS 5628:Part 2[4.10] where a simplified rectangular stress block is used. The corresponding values for k_1 and k_2 are 1 and 0.5 for this stress block, which can be substituted in Eqs 4.19 and 4.26. Similarly, as the code[4.10] is in limit state terms the values of f_m and f_{pb} must be replaced by f_k/γ_{mm} and f_{pb}/γ_{ms} respectively. Following the concrete design, this code assumes a blanket value of the failure strain of 0.0035 for all types of masonry, although a large variation of ultimate strain has been obtained in experiments on clay brickwork.[4.5, 4.11]

Comparison with Test Results of Brickwork Beams

To validate the theoretical method, a large number of brickwork[4.6] beams were tested to failure under four-point loading as shown in Fig. 4.4. To find the ultimate moment, the stress block factors k_1, k_2, the compressive strength f_m, the ultimate strain ϵ_{mu} and the stress–strain relationship of the tendons are required.

In the test beams, compression develops in the direction parallel to the bed joint. Hence, a number of brickwork prisms ($h/t = 4.4$) in 1:0.25:3 and 1:0.5:4.5 (cement:lime:sand) mortar representing the first top course of the beam (Fig. 4.5) were tested under axial compression to determine the values of the parameters mentioned above. The average values[4.5, 4.6, 4.11] of $k_1 = 0.64$ and $k_2 = 0.38$ were obtained from the non-dimensional curve, Fig. 4.6.

The stress–strain relationship of tendons were obtained in axial tension.

Using the values obtained from the prism test for the various parameters mentioned above, the ultimate moments of the beams were calculated from Eq. 4.26. These were compared with the beam test results,[4.6] which are shown in Table 4.1. Good agreement was found between experimental and theoretical results.

Fig. 4.4
Prestressed
brickwork beam
under test

Diagonal Tension and Shear Strength

In addition to bending, a transverse load on a beam produces shear. The distribution of the resulting shearing stresses on a transverse section of the beam is obtained by elastic theory. Although the theory is strictly applicable to beams of homogeneous materials, it could be used for a prestressed masonry beam uncracked in flexure with certain reservations.

The distribution of shear stress at a transverse section of a homogeneous beam is given by

$$v = \frac{VA\bar{Y}}{Ib} \qquad\qquad [4.27]$$

Fig. 4.5
Brickwork prisms

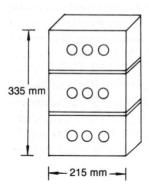

335 mm

|—— 215 mm ——|

$$f/f_m = 2.264\ (\epsilon/\epsilon_m) - 2.092\ (\epsilon/\epsilon_e)^2 + 0.834\ (\epsilon/\epsilon_m)^3$$

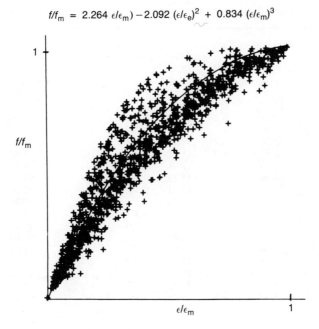

Fig. 4.6 Non-dimensional stress–strain relationship for brickwork

where v = shear stress;
      V = shear force at the section;
      $A\bar{Y}$ = first statical moment about the centroidal axis;
      I = second moment of area;
      b = width of the cross-section.

In the case of a rectangular section, the equation gives a parabolic shear stress distribution with the value of zero at top and bottom and a maximum at the centroidal axis of the beam. The value of the maximum shear stress is given by

$$v = 1.5\ \frac{V}{bd}.\qquad\qquad\qquad\text{[4.28]}$$

Let us consider an infinitesimal element as shown in Fig. 4.7 at the centroidal axis of a beam without prestress. It can be shown analytically or by Mohr's circle that the shear stresses give rise to maximum and minimum principal stresses, one compressive and the other tensile, always inclined at 45° to the longitudinal axis or to the bed joint of the beam. Their values will be equal to the shear stress. It is assumed that if the principal tensile stress reaches the tensile strength of the masonry, failure will take place in diagonal tension. In an uncracked prestressed masonry beam, an infinitesimal element at the centroid will be subjected

Table 4.1 Comparison of experimental and theoretical moments for prestressed brickwork beams[4.6]

Beam	Brick strength (N mm^{-2})	Brickwork strength (N mm^{-2})	Span (m)	a_v/d ratio	% steel	Effective prestress (kN)	Ultimate moment in kN m	
							Experimental	Theory
B1	88	32.56	6.2	11.21	0.274	133	56.94	54.32
B3	88	32.56	6.2	11.21	0.274	133	61.50	54.34
B4	88	32.56	6.2	11.21	0.274	144	58.40	54.39
B5	88	32.56	6.2	11.21	0.274	133	59.20	54.39
B6	88	32.56	6.2	11.21	0.274	152	58.80	54.37
BA3	88	32.56	6.2	11.21	0.441	216	74.81	72.50
BS1	88	32.56	6.2	11.21	0.548	194	87.20	94.75
BS2	88	32.56	6.2	11.21	0.548	202	92.20	94.97
A1	67	23.70	2.0	2.56	0.274	124	48.00	52.23
A3	67	23.70	3.2	5.02	0.274	124	46.00	52.23
A4	67	23.70	3.2	5.02	0.274	149	46.10	52.38
A7	67	23.70	6.0	10.80	0.274	134	53.40	52.34
A8	67	23.70	2.0	2.56	0.274	142	51.80	52.45
A9	67	23.70	6.2	11.20	0.274	134	54.10	52.34
A10	67	23.70	6.2	11.20	0.274	152	54.72	52.38
A11	67	23.70	6.2	11.20	0.274	129	56.30	52.35
1	67	23.70	6.0	9.70	0.255	152	61.40	58.65
2	67	23.70	2.0	2.30	0.255	141	49.50	58.65
3	67	23.70	4.4	6.82	0.255	124	49.40	58.73
4	67	23.70	4.4	6.82	0.255	154	57.00	58.80
5	67	23.70	3.2	4.61	0.255	140	56.00	58.77
6	67	23.70	3.2	4.61	0.510	303	71.10	90.90
7	67	23.70	2.0	2.30	0.510	287	67.80	90.10
AM1*	67	16.93	6.2	11.21	0.274	132	48.60	49.00
AM2*	67	16.93	6.2	11.21	0.274	127	45.80	47.83
AM4*	67	16.93	6.2	11.21	0.274	142	48.70	49.05
C1	34	9.37	6.2	11.21	0.274	75	46.00	36.11
C2	34	9.37	6.2	11.21	0.274	61	42.50	37.20
C3	34	9.37	6.2	11.21	0.274	119	54.10	40.25
D1	22	6.92	6.2	11.21	0.274	61	35.50	24.05
D2	22	6.92	6.2	11.21	0.274	72	25.80	24.76

* In 1:0.5:4.5 mortar. Rest in 1:0.25:3 mortar.

to shear stresses and normal compressive stress f_p due to prestress as shown in Fig. 4.8.

Under such biaxial stress conditions, the principal tensile stress at a point and its inclination to the axis or the bed joint of the beam is given by

$$f_t = \tfrac{1}{2} \sqrt{(f_p^2 + 4v^2)} + f_{p/2}$$ [4.29]

$$\theta = \tfrac{1}{2} \tan^{-1} \frac{2v}{f_p}.$$ [4.30]

Rearranging Eq. 4.29, we get

$$v = \sqrt{(f_t^2 + f_t f_p)}.$$ [4.31]

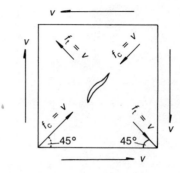

Fig. 4.7 An element subjected to pure shear

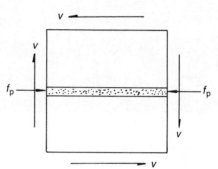

Fig. 4.8 An element in prestressed masonry subjected to biaxial stresses

Substituting the value of v in Eq. 4.28 gives

$$V = 0.67bd \sqrt{(f_t^2 + f_t f_p)}. \qquad [4.32]$$

By replacing b with b_w, the equation can also be used for a flanged beam with some loss of accuracy, since the maximum tensile stress may occur at the junction of web and tensile flange instead of the centroid. The design of a prestressed beam uncracked in flexure can be achieved by limiting the value of f_t in Eq. 4.32. The difficulty is to assign a value of f_t for masonry. It is known that under biaxial stress conditions,[4.12] i.e. compression−tension, the value of f_t not only depends on the ratios of the two stresses but also on the angle of inclination of the tensile stress to the bed joint. In the prestressed beam, the angle of inclination of the principal tensile stress at the centroid does not remain constant at 45° to the bed joint like a homogeneous beam but depends largely on the ratio $2v/f_p$ as given in Eq. 4.30. Additionally, the crack forms stepwise following the interface of brick and mortar in bed and collar joints, where the tensile strength is minimum and influenced by a large number of factors.[4.13]

In a flexurally cracked prestressed masonry beam, shear cracks develop as the extension of a flexural crack as shown in Fig. 4.9 which is for

Fig. 4.9 Failure of prestressed brickwork beam

a prestressed brickwork beam. The magnitude and distribution of shear stress in such a condition are not fully known. As in reinforced masonry[4.14, 4.15] many other factors may influence the ultimate shear strength of prestressed masonry. Hence, it would be appropriate, at present, to base the design on nominal ultimate shear stress[4.6, 4.7] given by

$$v = \frac{V}{bd}.$$ [4.33]

For prestressed brickwork beams, the value of nominal ultimate shear stress may be obtained from Fig. 4.1. The value thus obtained must be reduced by an appropriate factor of safety for the design.

Deflection

Both short- and long-term deflections must be checked in the case of prestressed masonry beams. The short-term deflection is due to the prestress and the service load consisting of dead plus live load. The deflection in the long term will increase due to creep, which must be considered in the design. Generally, the deflection due to creep is caused only by the permanent load, i.e. due to the prestress and dead weight. In case any part of the live load is of a permanent nature, the effect of creep must be considered. To calculate the long-term deflection, the short-term deflection due to the prestress plus dead weight or any permanent load is multiplied by a creep factor and the live load deflection is then added to it, i.e.

> Long-term deflection = $(1+\phi)$ × short-term deflection due to permanent load + live load deflection

where ϕ = creep factor.

In BS 5628,[4.10] the values of ϕ are given as 1.5 for clay and calcium silicate bricks and 3.0 for a dense concrete block. In unbonded prestressed brickwork beams built with 35 N mm^{-2} bricks in 1:0.25:3 mortar, the creep factor ϕ equal to 1.4 was recorded[4.16] in one year. Most of the creep deflection took place in the first 60 days of the application of the load.

The deflection of a beam can be calculated by any standard method, if no cracking is allowed under the service loading. Otherwise, a more rigorous method[4.17] given elsewhere may be used to calculate the deflection of prestressed masonry beams from cracking to failure.

Loss of Prestress

The reduction in the initially applied tension to the prestressing steel is often expressed as prestress loss. The prestress loss occurs as the result of the elastic deformation, slip of tendons at anchorage during anchoring, friction, moisture shrinkage and creep of masonry and the relaxation of steel.

Elastic Deformation Loss

When the prestressing force is released from the external abutments and transferred to the masonry elements, it causes compression and shortening of its length. As the length of the masonry reduces, so also does the steel. Therefore, the strain in the masonry must be equal to the change in the tensile strain in the steel. Consequently, there will be loss of prestress.

The loss of prestress due to elastic deformation can be calculated as follows, assuming: Δf_s is the loss of prestress in tendons at transfer, f'_m the masonry compressive stress at tendon level after transfer, and f_s the prestress immediately before transfer. From compatibility

$$\frac{\Delta f_s}{E_s} = \frac{f'_m}{E_m}$$

or

$$\Delta f_s = \frac{E_s}{E_m} f'_m = m f'_m \qquad [4.34]$$

where m is the modular ratio.

Stress in masonry at tendon level

$$f'_m = (f_s - \Delta f_s)A_{ps}\left(\frac{1}{A} + \frac{e_s^2}{I}\right). \tag{4.35}$$

Substituting the value of f'_m from Eq. 4.35 in 4.34 and rearranging,

$$\Delta f_s = \frac{mf_s\, A_{ps}\, (1/A + e_s^2/I)}{1 + m\, A_{ps}\, (1/A + e_s^2/I)}. \tag{4.36}$$

In prestressed concrete design,[4.2] the term

$$mA_{ps}\left(\frac{1}{A} + \frac{e_s^2}{I}\right)$$

works out to be very small, hence it is neglected and the prestress loss is obtained simply by

$$\Delta f_s = mf_s\, A_{ps}\left(\frac{1}{A} + \frac{e_s^2}{I}\right). \tag{4.37}$$

In masonry, if the simplified equation is used, the prestressing loss will be overestimated by 7−13 per cent.

During post-tensioning, the elastic shortening occurs as the tendons are stretched against the masonry. The tendons are locked off when the required prestress or extension of the tendons is achieved. Thus no loss of prestress occurs in post-tensioned masonry elements with single or multiple tendons if all the tendons are tensioned simultaneously in a single operation. However, if the tendons are tensioned in sequence, there will be loss of prestress due to elastic deformation in those tendon or tendons which were previously stressed.

Loss due to Slip at Anchorage

In post-tensioned elements, when the force is transferred from the jack to the end anchorage, there will be 'lock off' loss of prestress resulting from the movement of tendon and wedge draw-in. Such loss is appreciable in short post-tensioned elements. The loss cannot be assessed theoretically. The manufacturer of the particular anchorage system will be able to provide data from which the loss can be evaluated. In practice, this loss can be eliminated from the dead end by stressing the tendon and releasing the force without anchoring at the jacking end or compensated by overstressing. No such loss of prestress takes place in an anchorage which utilizes the threaded nut system for post-tensioning.

Friction Loss

In post-tensioning systems with the tendons in a duct, the prestressing force which is applied at the jacking end is reduced by the friction between the wall of the duct and the tendons. The loss of stress in the tendons increases with the distance from the jacking end and can be expressed as

$$f_{px} = f_{pj} \, e^{-kx} \qquad\qquad [4.38]$$

where f_{px} = stress at distance x from the jacking end;
$\quad\quad\;\; f_{pj}$ = stress in the tendon at the jacking end;
$\quad\quad\;\; e$ = base of Napierian logarithms;
$\quad\quad\;\; k$ = a coefficient depending on the type of duct;
$\quad\quad\;\; x$ = distance from jacking end.

In post-tensioned masonry, at present, only straight tendons are used and they are placed in a wide preformed cavity. Thus it is highly unlikely that the tendons will come into contact with the sides of the cavity during the stressing operation. Consequently, the loss of prestress due to friction will be negligible in these circumstances.

Moisture Expansion and Shrinkage Loss

It is known that fired clay brickwork suffers moisture expansion. In a prestressed brickwork element, the moisture expansion may therefore result in an increase of prestressing force in the tendons. Such an increase in prestress, however, is ignored in design. On the other hand, if moisture movement causes shrinkage of the masonry, there will be loss of prestress. The shrinkage loss can be evaluated as follows, assuming: Δf_{ss} is the loss of prestress in the tendon, Δf_{ms} the corresponding, in masonry stress at tendon level, and ϵ_{ms} the masonry shrinkage strain. From compatibility

$$\frac{\Delta f_{ss}}{E_s} = \epsilon_{ms} - \frac{\Delta f_{ms}}{E_m}. \qquad\qquad [4.39]$$

Stress at tendon level

$$\Delta f_{ms} = \Delta f_{ss} \, A_{ps} \left(\frac{1}{A} + \frac{e_s^2}{I} \right). \qquad\qquad [4.40]$$

Substituting the value Δf_{ms} from Eq. 4.40 in 4.39 and rearranging,

$$\Delta f_{ss} = \frac{E_s \epsilon_{ms}}{1 + m \, A_{ps} \, (1/A + e_s^2/I)}. \qquad\qquad [4.41]$$

The long-term shrinkage strain, ϵ_{ms}, equal to 500×10^{-6} for calcium silicate and concrete bricks, has been recommended.[4.10]

Creep Loss

In addition to shrinkage, loss of prestress must be considered as a result of the creep of masonry. The deformation of masonry due to creep is time-dependent and occurs at constant stress. The prestress loss due to creep of masonry can be calculated as

$$\Delta f_{sc} = \phi \, \frac{E_s}{E_m} \, f_{mi} = \phi m f_{mi} \qquad [4.42]$$

where ϕ = creep coefficient;
Δf_{sc} = loss of prestress due to creep;
f_{mi} = masonry stress at tendon level at transfer.

Values of the creep coefficient between 1.55 and 1.76 for brickwork walls have been reported.[4.16] Due to creep, the loss of prestress in relation to the initial prestress in post-tensioned brickwork was found[4.16] to vary from 11 to 15 per cent for walls, 8 to 10 per cent in columns and 12 per cent in beams. However, in all three cases the prestress was applied normal to and not parallel to the bed joint of the brickwork. As masonry possesses both stiffness and strength orthotropies, it is unlikely that these values can be applied universally. As there is less mortar in the parallel direction creep may be less, so this assumption may be regarded as conservative.

The British Standard[4.10] code for the structural use of reinforced and prestressed masonry recommends a blanket value of creep strain equal to 1.5 and 3 times the elastic strain for fired clay or calcium silicate and dense concrete block masonry respectively.

Relaxation Loss

Highly stressed steel maintained at constant length loses stress, which is expressed as relaxation loss. The loss takes place over a period of time and depends on various factors, such as type of steel, stress level and temperature. It is customary for the manufacturers of prestressing steel to quote 1000 hours relaxation value at an ambient temperature of 20 °C for the initial stress of 80, 70 and 60 per cent of its ultimate tensile strength. To compute the relaxation loss, the initial stress is taken immediately after stressing in pretensioning and at transfer for post-tensioning.

The relaxation, creep and shrinkage losses are time-dependent and interactive. Owing to this interaction, the British Standard[4.18] for structural use of concrete suggests multiplying the 1000 hours relaxation test value by the relaxation factors. The relaxation factors take into account the effects of deformations due to creep and shrinkage of concrete and, in pretensioning, the effect of elastic deformation at transfer. In the case of masonry, the prediction of combined loss due to creep, shrinkage and relaxation has been attempted by finite element analysis,[4.19] but no experimental data are available at present. Hence the losses due to creep, shrinkage and relaxation have to be worked out separately and added together, which is likely to result in an overestimate of the total loss.

Thermal Effect

In some situations in building, prestressed cavity walls or wide cavity cellular walls with unbonded tendons are used to counteract lateral pressure. The external wall in such construction undergoes wide temperature fluctuations and will generally be at a different temperature from the inner wall. As a result an unbonded tendon in the cavity will be subjected to different temperatures from the inner or outer walls due to the temperature gradient. Such a condition might lead to loss of precompression due to differential thermal movement. This should be considered in design.

References

4.1   Allen A H 1981 *An Introduction to Prestressed Concrete* 2nd edn Cement and Concrete Association, UK
4.2   Kong F K, Evans R H 1983 *Reinforced and Prestressed Concrete* 2nd edn Van Nostrand Reinhold (UK), London
4.3   Abeles P W 1964 *Introduction to Prestressed Concrete* Vol 1 Concrete Publications, London
4.4   Wass R J, Turner D J 1969 A prestressed clay masonry. In Johnson F B (ed) *Designing, Engineering and Constructing with Masonry Products* Gulf, Houston, Texas pp 200–9
4.5   Walker P J 1987 A study of the behaviour of partially prestressed brickwork beams. PhD thesis, Edinburgh University, UK
4.6   Pedreschi R F 1983 A study of the behaviour of post-tensioned brickwork beams. PhD thesis, Edinburgh University, UK
4.7   Pedreschi R F, Sinha B P 1986 The shear strength of prestressed brick beams. In West H W H (ed) *Proceedings of the British Masonry Society* Masonry 1, Stoke-on-Trent Nov 1986 pp 114–16
4.8   Uduehi J 1989 Comparative study of the behaviour of prestressed brickwork and concrete beams and the shear strength of partially prestressed brickwork beams. PhD thesis, University of Edinburgh, UK
4.9   Hendry A W, Sinha B P, Davies S R 1987 *Load Bearing Brickwork Design* 2nd edn Ellis Horwood, UK
4.10 British Standards Institution 1985 *British Standard Code of Practice for*

Use of Masonry BS 5628 Part 2 Structural Use of Reinforced and Prestressed Masonry London

4.11   Sinha B P, Pedreschi R F 1983 Compressive strength and some elastic properties of brickwork. *The International Journal of Masonry Construction* **3**(1): 19—25

4.12   Page A W 1983 The strength of brick masonry under bi-axial tension compression. *The International Journal of Masonry Construction* **3**(1): 26—31

4.13   Sinha BP 1983 Factors affecting the brick/mortar interface bond strength. *The International Journal of Masonry Construction* **3**(1): 14—18

4.14   Hendry A W 1990 *Structural Masonry* Macmillan, London

4.15   Sinha B P 1982 Reinforced grouted cavity brickwork. *Building Research and Practice* **10**(4) July/Aug: 226—43

4.16   Lenczner D 1985 The loss of prestress in post-tensioned brick masonry member. *Masonry International* **5**: 9—12

4.17   Pedreschi R F, Sinha B P 1985 Deformation and cracking of post-tensioned brickwork beams. *Structural Engineer* **63B**(4) Dec

4.18   British Standards Institution 1985 *Structural Use of Concrete BS 8110 Part 1 Code of Practice for Design and Construction* London

4.19   Shrive N G 1988 Effects of time dependent movements in composite and post-tensioned masonry. *Masonry International* **2**(1): 23—9

5 Reinforced Masonry Compression Elements

Dr S R Davies, University of Edinburgh

Introduction

Masonry elements subjected to compressive loading have not been studied experimentally to the same extent as other elements of reinforced masonry. This is not peculiar to masonry since a similar situation exists with respect to reinforced concrete. The situation arises because of the difficulty of representing the end conditions of the supports in a realistic way and then expressing these conditions mathematically.

Elements in compression can be divided into a number of categories which depend on the slenderness of the member and the type of loading. With regard to slenderness, columns can be classed as 'short' or 'slender'. Loading can be axial, uniaxial bending or biaxial bending.

The theoretical approach tends to follow the methods developed for reinforced concrete with appropriate changes introduced to allow for the different material properties.

Effect of Slenderness

Slenderness Ratio

The slenderness ratio of a compressive element can be defined as the ratio of a length parameter and a cross-sectional parameter. As far as masonry is concerned these parameters, for rectangular sections, are effective height and effective depth. For other shapes radius of gyration might be more appropriate.

Effective Height

The effective height of a wall or column is the distance between points of zero moment and, since this depends on the support conditions, there may be a difference between the value obtained assuming ideal support conditions and that which occurs in practice. Relevant codes of practice suggest values that can be used for different support conditions.

Taking h as the clear distance between supports, the British code[5.1] BS 5628 recommends values of h or $0.75h$ for walls with lateral support top and bottom depending on the assumed degree of partial fixity resulting from the number of floors framing into the support. For columns, if the lateral support restricts the moment along both the major and minor axis, a value of h is suggested. If movement restriction is along one axis then a value of h is used for the restrained axis and $2h$ for the unrestrained.

Effective Thickness

The effective thickness of a wall or column is related to the actual thickness and, for single-leaf walls and columns, these thicknesses are taken to be the same in BS 5628. For cavity walls with only one leaf reinforced, the effective thickness is taken as the greater of either the thickness of the thicker leaf or two-thirds of the sum of the thicknesses of both leaves.

For grouted cavity walls the effective thickness is defined as the overall thickness of the wall, provided that the cavity width does not exceed 100 mm. If it does then only 100 mm of the cavity is included in the calculation.

Limits of Slenderness Ratio

There are two limits to slenderness ratio for both walls and columns. One is the limit which separates short elements from those of slender elements and the other the upper limit beyond which the element would be too slender for stability. Suggested upper limits are 18 for cantilever elements and 27 for others. Short columns and walls are defined as those for which the slenderness ratio does not exceed 12.

These limits are required because of the lateral deflections which increase with slenderness, thereby increasing the overall eccentricity. This in turn reduces the load-carrying capacity of the element because of the additional moment introduced. In very slender elements the additional eccentricity can be so large that the failure mode changes from material failure to instability failure.

Basic Assumptions

Stress and Strain Relationships

The assumed stress—strain relationships will be a simplification of those which occur in practice, and for brickwork the usual simplified parabolic stress—strain relationship is further simplified, for compressive elements,

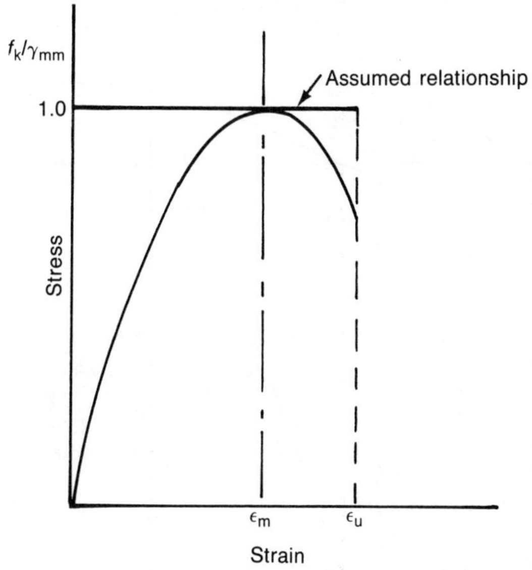

Fig. 5.1 Idealized stress–strain relationship for brickwork

f_k/γ_{mm}

Assumed relationship

1.0

Stress

ϵ_m ϵ_u

Strain

into the rectangular form shown in Fig. 5.1. It is also usual to assume that the stress–strain relationship for any grouting material is the same as that for brickwork.

Similarly, the stress–strain relationship for steel is assumed to be trilinear as shown in Fig. 5.2. The value of the strain at the points marked A and B depends on the value of f_y and γ_{ms}, the characteristic strength and partial safety factor for the reinforcement respectively. Values of these strains are shown on the diagram for two typical steels.

Additional Assumptions

In addition to the assumed form of the stress–strain diagrams additional assumptions are made as follows:

(a) Plane sections before bending remain plane after bending.
(b) Any tensile strength in the masonry is ignored.
(c) The strains in both materials are directly proportional to the distances from the neutral axis.
(d) The maximum strain in the outermost compression fibre at failure is 0.0035.

From the stress–strain relationship for masonry and assumption (d) the maximum compressive stress in the masonry is f_k/γ_{mm}, where f_k is the characteristic strength of the brickwork and γ_{mm} the partial safety factor.

It will be shown later that one of the main difficulties with the design

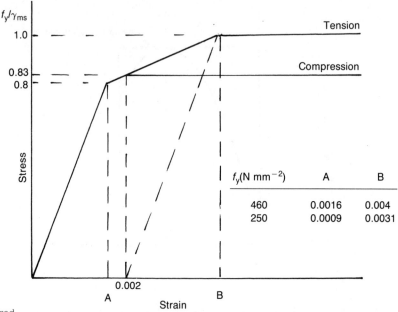

$f_y(\text{N mm}^{-2})$	A	B
460	0.0016	0.004
250	0.0009	0.0031

Fig. 5.2 Idealized stress–strain relationship for reinforcement

of columns under axial load and bending is the determination of the stress, f_{2s}, in the reinforcement near the least compressed, or tensile, face. This stress is a function of the neutral axis depth which is unknown initially. Different values for the depth of the neutral axis can be assumed at the discretion of the designer, each leading to different solution sets for N_d, the design axial load resistance, and M_d the design moment resistance.

The Stress in the Reinforcement

As shown in Fig. 5.3, there are two cases to consider depending on whether the assumed neutral axis depth results in a tensile or compressive stress in the lower steel. For both cases the strain ϵ_2 is given by

$$\epsilon_2 = 0.0035(t - d_c - d_2)/d_c \tag{5.1}$$

where the symbols used are as illustrated in Fig. 5.3 and a distinction is made between positive tensile and negative compressive strain.

Using the assumed value of d_c, and a trial section, the value of ϵ_2 can now be calculated and the stress in the reinforcement determined from the stress–strain diagram. The procedure is as follows:

1. From the trial section both t and d_2 are known.
2. Assume a value of d_c and calculate ϵ_2 from Eq. 5.1.
3. Use this value of ϵ_2, and the stress–strain diagram, to determine the value of f_{2s}.

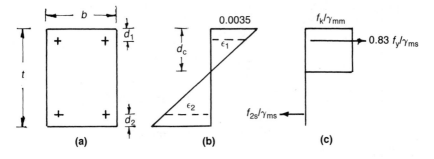

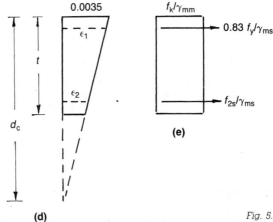

Fig. 5.3 Two
cases of
distribution of
strain and stress in
cross-section:
(a) cross-section;
(b) strain diagram;
(c) stress diagram;
(d) strain diagram;
(e) stress diagram

The calculation is dependent on f_y as well as d_2 and diagrams showing the variation of the ratio f_{2s}/f_y with the ratio d_c/t are given in Figs 5.4 and 5.5 for two values of d_2. The three curves shown in the diagrams represent the ratios for $f_y = 460$ N mm^{-2}, $f_y = 250$ N mm^{-2} and the values obtained using BS 5628. The latter are based on additional simplifying assumptions used in the British code which makes the curve independent of f_y. These assumptions can be expressed as follows:

(a) d_c is assumed to be greater than $2d_1$.
(b) If d_c is chosen to be between $2d_1$ and $t/2$ then f_{2s} is taken as equal to f_y.
(c) If d_c is chosen between $t/2$ and $t-d_2$ then f_{2s} is found by interpolation using the formula

$$f_{2s} = 2f_y(t-d_2-d_c)/(t-d_2). \qquad [5.2]$$

(d) If d_c is chosen between $t-d_2$ and t then f_{2s} is taken as 0.

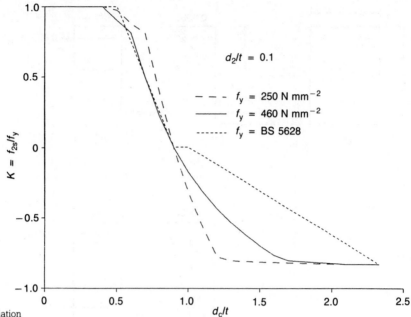

Fig. 5.4 Variation of *K* with d_c/t for $d_2/t = 0.1$

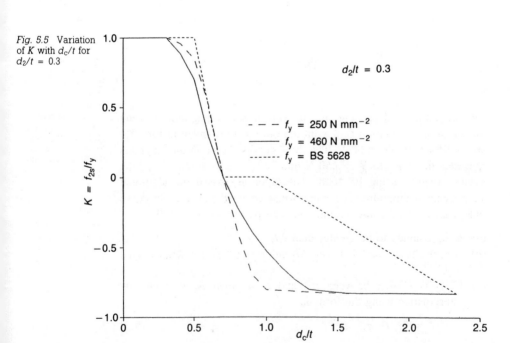

Fig. 5.5 Variation of *K* with d_c/t for $d_2/t = 0.3$

(e) If d_c is taken as greater than t then the stress in A_{s2} will be compressive and will vary between 0 and $-0.83f_y/\gamma_{ms}$.

(f) It is also assumed that the strain in the reinforcement nearest to the most highly compressed face will be greater than 0.002 so that the stress in this reinforcement will be equal to $0.83f_y/\gamma_{ms}$ (Fig. 5.2).

Short Columns

As far as design procedures are concerned, this class of column is further subdivided into cases where the bending is either uniaxial or biaxial.

The basic assumptions given in this chapter apply to cross-sections of any shape and, for any particular cross-section, it would be possible to use these assumptions to design an element from first principles. Fortunately, symmetrical arrangements of reinforcement in rectangular sections are the more usual case in brickwork and advantage can be taken of this with a resulting simplification.

Note on Non-dimensional Approach

Three non-dimensional parameters related to axial load, bending moment and area of reinforcement are defined as follows:

$$L = N\gamma_{mm}/f_k bt \qquad\qquad\qquad [5.3]$$

$$B = M\gamma_{mm}/f_k bt^2 \qquad\qquad\qquad [5.4]$$

$$S = f_y\gamma_{mm}\rho/f_k\gamma_{ms} \qquad\qquad\qquad [5.5]$$

where ρ represents the total area of the steel divided by the area of the section.

Using Eqs 5.3 and 5.4 it can be shown that the non-dimensional form of the eccentricity is represented by

$$B/L = \epsilon_x/t$$

Additionally, a factor K is defined such that

$$f_{2s} = Kf_y. \qquad\qquad\qquad [5.6]$$

This factor, K, is illustrated in Figs 5.4 and 5.5 for two values of f_y and also the values obtained from BS 5628.

Uniaxial Bending

Case 1: Low Values of Axial Load

This case is used for situations where the axial load is below a specified value. A limit is also implied for the value of the design moment since the ratio M/N, which appears in the equation in the form ϵ_x, is not allowed to exceed $0.5t$.

If the applied axial load N does not exceed the value of the design axial load resistance N_d given by

$$N_d = f_k b(t-2\epsilon_x)/\gamma_{mm} \qquad [5.7]$$

then only a minimum of reinforcement is required and design in accordance with the principles of unreinforced sections is considered more appropriate.

The condition for the applicability of case 1, viz.

$$N < N_d = f_k b(t-2\epsilon_x)/\gamma_{mm}$$

can be expressed in non-dimensional form as

$$L < L_d = 1-2B/L. \qquad [5.8]$$

Case 2: General Case

If the design axial load is greater than the value given by Eq. 5.7 then expressions for both axial load and moment must be derived in order to relate all the relevant parameters.

Using the basic assumptions given on pages 100−102 and determining the total axial force carried by the brickwork in compression and also by the steel, the following equation for the design axial resistance can be derived:

$$N_d = f_k b d_c/\gamma_{mm} + 0.83 f_y A_{s1}/\gamma_{ms} - f_{2s} A_{s2}/\gamma_{ms}. \qquad [5.9]$$

Similarly, by taking moment about the mid-section of the forces in the steel and the compressive brickwork, an expression can be obtained for the design moment of resistance (M_d):

$$M_d = 0.5 f_k \, b d_c \, (t-d_c)/\gamma_{mm} + 0.83 f_y \, A_{s1} \, (0.5t-d_1)/\gamma_{ms}$$
$$-f_{2s} \, A_{s2} \, (0.5t-d_2)/\gamma_{ms} \qquad [5.10]$$

The meaning of most of the symbols used in these equations has been given previously; others are illustrated in Fig. 5.6.

For asymmetrical sections these equations must be solved by first assuming trial sections and areas of reinforcement and then determining f_{2s} for an assumed value of d_c in accordance with the assumptions outlined on page 102. From the assumed value of d_c, the value of f_{2s} can be determined and the equations can be solved for N_d and M_d using the values of the trial section. These values of N_d and M_d must be greater respectively than the applied load (N) and applied moment (M), otherwise new values of d_c and/or trial section must be tried and the process repeated.

This process can be quite tedious and, for doubly reinforced rectangular

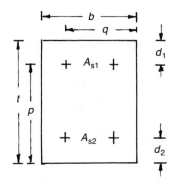

Fig. 5.6 Cross-sectional details

sections with a symmetrical arrangement of the reinforcement, interaction diagrams can be drawn which permit a direct solution of the equations.

Using Eqs 5.4–5.6 the basic equations 5.9 and 5.10 can be rewritten into the simplified forms

$$L_d = d_c/t + S(0.415 - 0.5K) \qquad [5.11]$$

$$B_d = 0.5(d_c/t)\,(1 - d_c/t) + S\{4(0.415 + 0.5K)\,(0.5 - d_1/t)\} \qquad [5.12]$$

and these equations used to construct design interaction charts.

Chart Details Before the charts are drawn a decision has to be made as to which value of K is to be used. If K is based on BS 5628 then the charts would be independent of f_y and therefore fewer charts would be required. If K is based on f_y then a set of charts is required for each value of this characteristic strength. To illustrate the influence of the K-value used, sample curves for two types of steel and also using the BS 5628 approach are shown in Figs 5.7 and 5.8. The figures are plotted for d_1/t equal to 0.1 in Fig. 5.7 and 0.3 in Fig. 5.8. It is apparent from these figures that the curves, for particular values of S and d_1/t, are similar for all values of d_c/t less than 0.8.

From these plots it can be assumed that the curves for f_y equal to 460 N mm^{-2} can be used to represent all steels for values of d_c/t less than 0.8. If the curve for f_y equal to 250 N mm^{-2} is also drawn for values of d_c/t greater than 0.8 then any required correction for different f_y values can be made by eye. This is the approach used to represent the interaction diagrams shown in charts 1–5 (Figs 5.9–5.14).

The charts are drawn for values of $d_1/t = 0.1, 0.15, 0.2, 0.25$ and 0.3 and a doubly reinforced symmetrical rectangular section is assumed. They apply to all values of f_y, γ_{mm} and γ_{ms} so that the number of charts required is reduced from the number usually presented. In each chart the load parameter is plotted against the bending parameter for a range of values of S, the steel parameter.

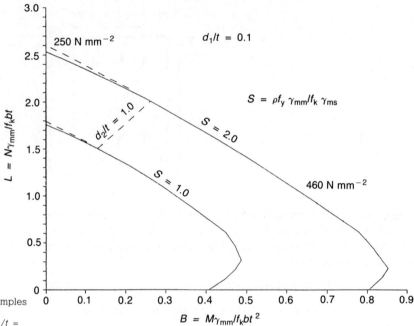

Fig. 5.7 Examples of interaction curves for $d_1/t = 0.1$

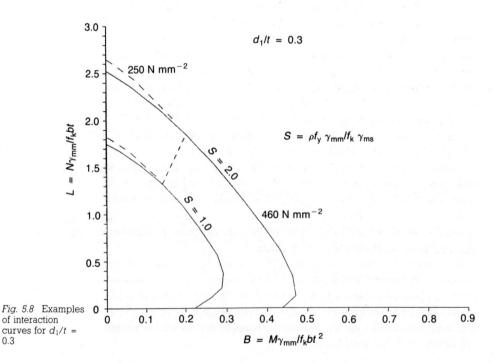

Fig. 5.8 Examples of interaction curves for $d_1/t = 0.3$

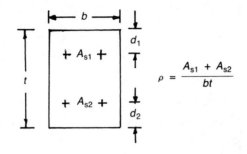

Fig. 5.9 Key to charts

$$\rho = \frac{A_{s1} + A_{s2}}{bt}$$

$$L = N\,\gamma_{mm}/f_k bt$$
$$B = M\,\gamma_{mm}/f_k bt^2$$
$$S = \rho\, f_y\, \gamma_{mm}/f_k\, \gamma_{ms}$$

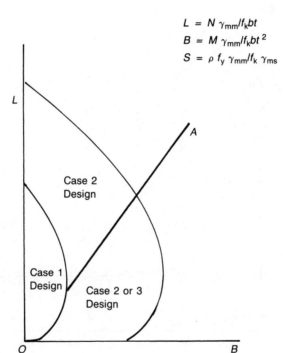

To illustrate the method of construction consider chart 1 (Fig. 5.10) for which $d_1/t = 0.1$ and let $d_c/t = 0.5$. For this value of d_c/t the value of K can be determined as explained above but, for purposes of illustration, assume that the value of K is based on BS 5628, and therefore equal to 1, so that Eqs 5.11 and 5.12 become

$$L_d = 0.5 - 0.085S \qquad\qquad [5.13]$$

$$B_d = 0.125 + 0.366S \qquad\qquad [5.14]$$

which can be solved for any value of S as shown in the following examples:

Fig. 5.10 Chart 1

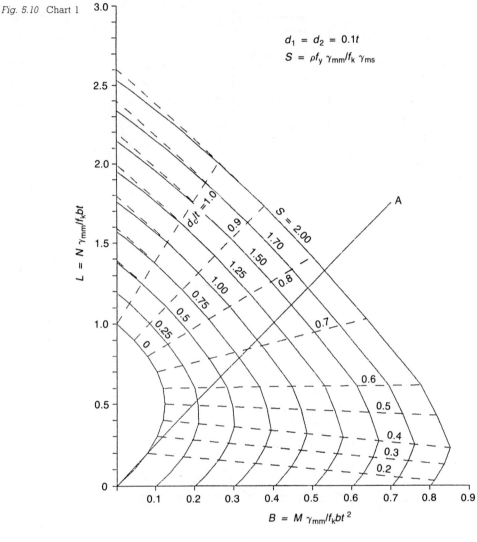

$$B = M \, \gamma_{mm}/f_k bt^2$$

S	0	0.25	1.0	2.0
L_d	0.5	0.479	0.5	0.33
B_d	0.125	0.216	0.491	0.857

These are typical values of $d_c/t = 0.5$, and K based on BS 5628, but obviously a similar approach can be used for other values of d_c/t, K and S.

Application to Case 1 (page 105) If S is equated to zero in Eqs 5.11 and 5.12 we obtain

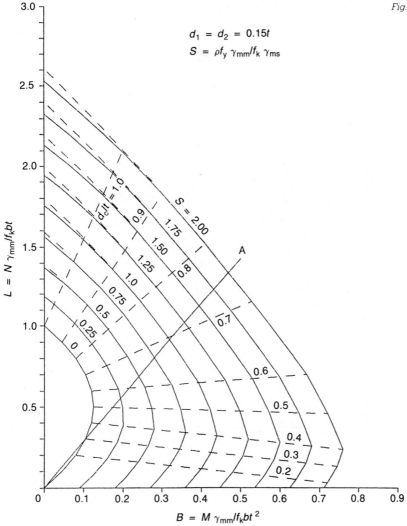

Fig. 5.11 Chart 2

$$L_d = d_c/t$$

and

$$B_d = 0.5(d_c/t)(1-d_c/t).$$

Eliminating d_c/t from these equations it can be shown that

$$L_d = 1-2B_d/L_d$$

which is similar to Eq. 5.8, the limiting equation for the application of case 1, so that case 1 is implied by the equations representing case 2.

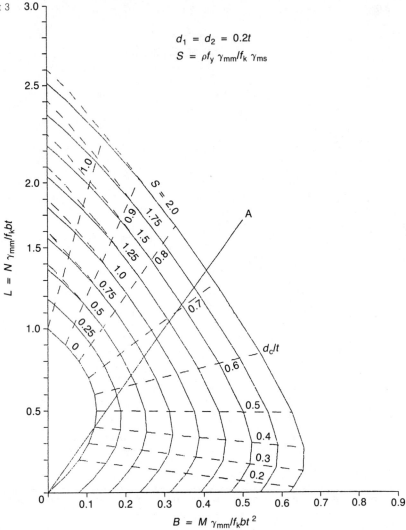

Fig. 5.12 Chart 3

Note that although an acceptable solution is obtained when $L_d > L$ and $B_d > B$, a more efficient solution exists if $L_d = L$ and $B_d = B$.

Case 3: Large Eccentricities

If the eccentricity, M/N, exceeds the value $(t/2 - d_1)$ then an alternative approach to that given on page 106 is required. In this case the axial load may be ignored and the section designed to resist an increased moment. This increased moment is given by the formula

$$M_a = M + N(t/2 - d_1).$$ [5.15]

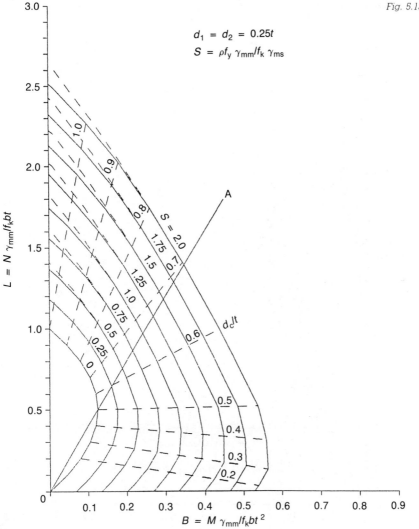

Fig. 5.13 Chart 4

Additionally, when using this method, the tension reinforcement necessary to provide resistance to this increased moment may be reduced by $N\gamma_{ms}/f_y$.

Equation 5.15 can be conveniently expressed in the non-dimensional notation defined in Eqs 5.3 and 5.4 so that the use of the charts can be extended to this case. Using B_a to represent the increased non-dimensional moment the equation becomes

$$B_a = B + L(0.5 - d_1/t) \qquad [5.16]$$

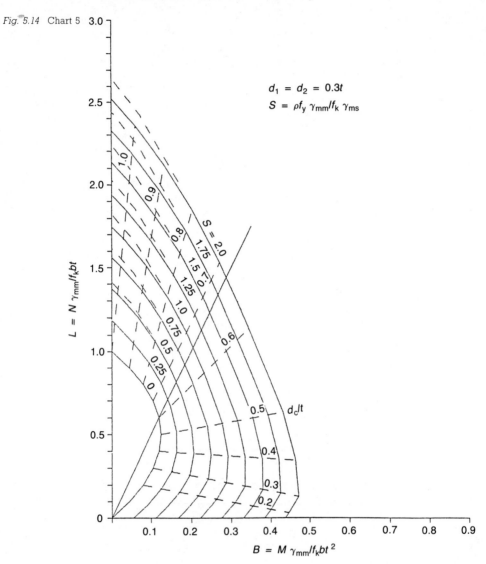

Fig. 5.14 Chart 5

and the condition for application of this case

$$\epsilon_x/t = B/L > (0.5 - d_1/t).\qquad\qquad [5.17]$$

Illustrative Examples
In order to illustrate the use of the charts and also to show the differences between the three cases given above, five examples are solved using the same value of applied axial load throughout but varying the value of applied moment so that the required solutions move through the three

Table 5.1

No.		Example				
		1	2	3	4	5
1	N(kN)	625	625	625	625	625
2	M(kN m)	62.5	78.125	93.75	125	187.5
3	L	0.5	0.5	0.5	0.5	0.5
4	B	0.1	0.125	0.15	0.2	0.3
5	S	0	0	0.07	0.2	0.5
6	$\rho(10^3)$	0	0	8.75	2.5	6.25
7	B/L	0.2	0.25	0.3	0.4	0.6
8	L_d	0.6	0.5	0.4	0.2	−0.2
9	$0.5 - d_1/t$	0.4	0.4	0.4	0.4	0.4
10	Case	1	1	2	2	3

cases. By selecting a constant value of N it is easy to follow the progress of the solutions as the value of M is increased. Other than the change in the value of M all other parameters remain constant and the values used are

$$b = t = 500 \text{ mm}, \qquad d_1 = d_2 = 50 \text{ mm},$$
$$f_k = 10 \text{ N mm}^{-2}, \qquad f_y = 460 \text{ N mm}^{-2},$$
$$\gamma_{mm} = 2, \qquad \gamma_{ms} = 1.15.$$

Using these values the results obtained, for a number of parameters and for each example, are listed in Table 5.1. Each line of the table is numbered for ease of reference in the discussion that follows.

The factors for converting lines 1 and 2 into lines 3 and 4 are obtained from the definitions of L and B given in Eqs 5.3 and 5.4. Since $d_1/t = 0.1$ chart 1 (Fig. 5.10) is used to read off the value of S and Eq. 5.5 used to convert this value to the steel ratio. These values are shown in lines 5 and 6. Normally this completes the solution of each example but lines 7–10 have been included in order to illustrate that the examples belong to the different cases described on pages 105–114. Line 7 can be obtained by dividing line 4 by line 3 and line 8 follows from Eq. 5.8. Line 9 relates to the limiting condition for case 3 as given in Eq. 5.17. Recalling the equations that define the limiting conditions for the three cases

Case 1 $L \quad < 1 - 2B/L$ $\qquad\qquad\qquad\qquad$ [5.8]

Case 2 $L \quad > 1 - 2B/L \quad \text{and} \quad B/L < 0.5 - d_1/t$
$\qquad\qquad\qquad\qquad\qquad\qquad\qquad$ [5.8], [5.17]

Case 3 $B/L > 0.5 - d_1/t$ $\qquad\qquad\qquad\qquad$ [5.17]

it is possible to show to which case the examples belong.

Comparing lines 3 and 8 of Table 5.1 it is apparent that example 1 belongs to case 1 and example 2 is at the limit of case 1. Note that although no reinforcement is required for this case, BS 5628 suggests a minimum value (see page 106). Examples 3 and 4 belong to case 2 with example 4 at the limit since B/L is equal to $(0.5 - d_1/t)$. This limiting position has been drawn on each chart as the line OA. Values of the sets N_d, M_d falling to the right of this line can be designed using either case 2 or case 3 methods. In example 5 B/L is greater than $(0.5 - d_1/t)$ so that this example belongs to case 3. Example 5 can therefore be solved using either case 2 or case 3.

To design the column of example 5 in accordance with case 2 principles the charts can be used directly and the result is as shown in Table 5.1. To design in accordance with case 3 principles the following steps have to be taken:

1. Increase the value of B by $L(0.5 - d_1/t)$ (Eq. 5.16). This would mean increasing B from 0.3 to 0.5 in example 5.
2. The axial load parameter is now ignored and design based on the increased value of B. The charts can still be used but, since L is now taken as 0, the B-axis must be used for determining S. This gives a value of $S = 1.25$ for example 5.
3. Decrease the area of the tensile steel by $N\gamma_{ms}/f_y$.

Summary of the Use of the Charts

The charts can be used for the three cases of design outlined in the section on uniaxial bending. Additionally, since the limiting conditions for the application of the three cases is indicated on the charts the designer is immediately aware of which set of design rules should be applied.

For any set of values of L, B:

1. If the point falls in the region to the left of the curve represented by $S = 0$ then case 1 applies and only a minimum amount of reinforcement is required or the column designed as an unreinforced section.
2. If the point falls between the curve $S = 0$ and the line OA then case 2 applies and the amount of reinforcement determined from the interpolated value of S at the point.
3. If the point falls to the right of OA then either case 2 or case 3 can be applied. Case 2 design is as for (2) above, while case 3 requires an increase in the value of B and the use of the B-axis to determine the value of S. For case 3 there would also be a reduction in the amount of tensile steel as explained on page 113.

Interaction diagrams are derived from theoretical considerations and there is not a great deal of experimental evidence to confirm that practical

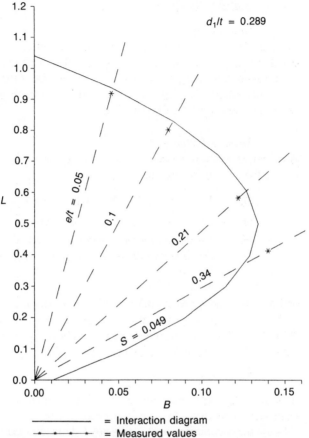

Fig. 5.15
Comparison
between
measured values[5.2]
and interaction
diagrams

——————— = Interaction diagram

—*—*—*— = Measured values

reinforced brickwork columns behave, under load, as predicted by these diagrams. However, Anderson and Hoffman,[5.2] reported the results of a series of tests on reinforced brickwork columns having the following properties:

$$b = 304.8 \text{ mm}, \qquad t = 406.4 \text{ mm}, \qquad d_1 = 117.5 \text{ mm},$$
$$f_k = 36.2 \text{ N mm}^{-2}, \quad f_y = 275.8 \text{ N mm}^{-2}, \quad A_2 = 804.2 \text{ mm}^2,$$

so that $d_1/t = 0.289$ and (with γ_{mm} and $\gamma_{ms} = 1.0$) $S = 0.049$. Four eccentricities were used for the tests and a comparison of the results with those obtained theoretically are shown in Fig. 5.15 where each test result represents the average result from three similar tests. Agreement between test results and interaction diagrams is quite good.

There is also indirect confirmation of the validity of these diagrams in that they have been used for some considerable time for reinforced concrete.

Biaxial Bending

Uniaxial Approach

In the British code it is stated that, even when significant moments occur simultaneously about both axes, it is generally sufficient to design for the uniaxial case using the maximum moment about the critical axis. Accepting this, the design procedure outlined in the previous section would also apply to the biaxial case.

Moment Increase

An alternative design method is based on increasing the moment about one of the axes in accordance with

$$M_{x'} = M_x + \alpha(p/q)M_y \quad \text{for } M_x/p > M_y/q \qquad [5.18]$$

$$M_{y'} = M_y + \alpha(q/p)M_x \quad \text{for } M_x/p < M_y/q \qquad [5.19]$$

where M_x = the design moment about the x-axis;
    $M_{x'}$ = the effective uniaxial design moment about the
        x-axis;
    p = $t - d_1$,

and M_y, $M_{y'}$ and q are similar terms with respect to the y-axis.

This method is similar to that proposed for reinforced concrete in BS 8110.[5.3] The value α to be used in the above equations is based on the ratio N/N_{dz} where N_{dz} is defined by

$$N_{dz} = f_k A_m \qquad [5.20]$$

in which A_m represents the area of the complete section. The relationship between N/N_{dz} and α is given in tabular form (Table 5.2).

Using the non-dimensional parameter L defined in Eq. 5.3, the ratio N/N_{dz} is equal to L/γ_{mm}, and therefore the use of the charts can be extended to cover the biaxial case. Defining B_x and B_y as the non-dimensional parameters representing M_x and M_y respectively, the steps necessary for this are:

1. Determine the value of α from Table 5.2 using L/γ_{mm}.
2. If B_x/p is $\geq B_y/q$ then increase B_x by an amount calculated using $\alpha(p/q)B_y$ and determine the value of S from L and the increased value of B_x. The appropriate chart to use is the one for which d_1 relates to the depth t.
3. If B_x/p is $< B_y/q$ then increase B_y by an amount calculated using $\alpha(q/p)B_x$ and determine the value of S from L and the increased value of B_y. The appropriate chart to use is the one for which d_1 relates to the breadth b.

Illustrative Examples

Following a similar approach to that used on page 115 two examples

Table 5.2

N/N_{dz}	α
0	1.00
0.1	0.88
0.2	0.77
0.3	0.65
0.4	0.53
0.5	0.42
>0.6	0.30

Table 5.3

		Example	
No.		6	7
1	N(kN)	625	625
2	M_x(kN m)	187.5	187.5
3	M_y(kN m)	125	187.5
4	L	0.5	0.5
5	B_x	0.3	0.3
6	B_y	0.2	0.3
7	$B_x/p\,(10^4)$	6.67	6.67
8	$B_y/q\,(10^4)$	5.0	7.5
9	Inc. in B_x	0.16	—
10	Inc. in B_y	—	0.19
11	$B_{x'}$	0.46	—
12	$B_{y'}$	—	0.49
13	Chart	1	3
14	S	0.96	1.41

are solved using the same value of axial load and bending about the x-axis but varying the bending moment abut the y-axis. Other parameters remain constant and the values used are:

b $= t = 500$ mm, $f_k = 10$ N mm^{-2}, $f_y = 460$ N mm^{-2},
d_1 $= d_2 = 50$ mm perpendicular to the x-axis, $p = 450$ mm,
d_1 $= d_2 = 100$ mm perpendicular to the y-axis, $q = 400$ mm,
$\gamma_{mm} = 2$, $\gamma_{ms} = 1.15$.

Values of N, M_x and M_y for the two examples are shown in Table 5.3 which also shows the values of the other calculated parameters.

Since, for both examples, $L = 0.5$ and $\gamma_{mm} = 2$, it follows using Table 5.2 that $\alpha = 0.71$. Using this value of α it follows that $\alpha p/q = 0.8$ and $\alpha q/p = 0.63$.

In example 6, lines 7 and 8 show that B_x/p is $> B_y/q$ and an increase must be calculated for B_x in line 9 using (0.8 × 0.2). The value $B_{x'}$ in line 11 is the sum of B_x plus this increase.

Fig. 5.16 Surface
of interaction

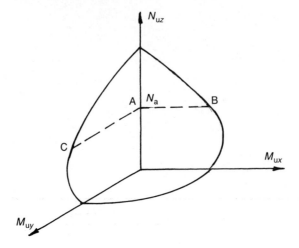

Fig. 5.17 Section
through interaction
surface

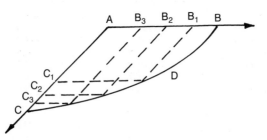

Similarly, in example 7, lines 7 and 8 show that $B_x/p < B_y/q$ so that
the increase must be calculated in B_y. This increase is found using (0.63×0.3), i.e. $\alpha(p/q)B_x$. The increased value of B_y is shown in line 12.

To find S chart 1 (Fig. 5.10) must be used for example 6, since $d_1/t = 0.1$, and chart 3 (Fig. 5.12) for example 7 since $d_1/t = 0.2$.

Alternative Approach

Combinations of the ultimate loads N_{uz}, M_{ux} and M_{uy} can be represented
by the surface shown in Fig. 5.16. This surface can be considered to
consist of a family of load contours for different values of the ultimate
axial load N_{uz}. For a particular value of N_{uz}, say N_a, a horizontal plane
can be drawn to intersect the N_{uz}–M_{ux} and N_{uz}–M_{uy} curves at points
B and C respectively, where AB and AC represent the maximum uniaxial
bending moments, about x and y, that can be applied together with N_a.
For the biaxial case different combinations of the moments can be defined,
as shown in Fig. 5.17, such as AB_1, AC_1; AB_2, AC_2; etc.

The curve CDB in Fig. 5.17 is elliptical and, in CP 110,[5.4, 5.5] has
been represented by the equation

$$\left(\frac{M_x}{M_{ux}} \right)^{\beta} + \left(\frac{M_y}{M_{uy}} \right)^{\beta} \leq 1 \qquad [5.21]$$

where M_x and M_y are the moments about the major and minor axes, and M_{ux} is the maximum moment capacity assuming ultimate axial load and bending about the major axis. M_{uy} is similar to M_{ux} but with bending about the minor axis. β is an exponent which depends on factors such as column dimensions, amount and distribution of reinforcement, stress–strain relationships and the amount of cover to the reinforcement. In CP 110 the exponent β is related to N/N_{uz} and values are given for a range of values of N/N_{uz}.

Davies and El-Traify[5.6, 5.7] have shown how this approach can also be used for brickwork if the value of N_{uz} is suitably modified. Working with design loads rather than ultimate loads and using the non-dimensional notation defined above the method can be summarized as follows.

Equation 5.21 can be rewritten in the form

$$\left(\frac{B_x}{B_{dx}} \right)^{\beta} + \left(\frac{B_y}{B_{dy}} \right)^{\beta} \leq 1 \qquad [5.22]$$

where B_x and B_y relate to the applied moments, and B_{dx} and B_{dy} relate to the design moments. The value of β depends on L/γ_{mm} and values are given in Table 5.4.

As an illustration of the use of this method consider the examples given on page 119.

Since $L/\gamma_{mm} = 0.25$, from Table 5.4 $\beta = 1.08$. The first three rows of each example in Table 5.5 are the same as the values given for examples 6 and 7 (page 119).

In order to find B_{dx} and B_{dy} a trial value of S must first be assumed and, using this value together with the value of L, this enables the value of B to be read from the appropriate chart. The appropriate chart for obtaining B_{dx} is the chart for which d_1/t is measured in the direction of t. For B_{dy}, the chart will be the one for which d_1/t is measured in the direction of b. Three trial values of S are shown, for example 6a, and two trial values for 7a. The first trial value for each example is the same as that found by the method described on page 119. Rows 7 and 8 show the ratios required for Eq. 5.22 and rows 9 and 10 show these ratios raised to the power β.

For Eq. 5.22 to be satisfied the sum of the quantities in lines 9 and 10 should be ≤ 1. This is not the case for the steel ratios assumed in

Table 5.4

L/γ_{mm}	≤ 0.2	0.4	0.6	≥ 0.8
β	1.0	1.33	1.67	2.0

Table 5.5

Row No.	Example	Column No.				
		1	2 6a	3	4 7a	5
1	L		0.5		0.5	
2	B_x		0.3		0.3	
3	B_y		0.2		0.3	
4	S	0.96	1.10	1.25	1.41	1.5
5	B_{dx}	0.46	0.51	0.56	0.61	0.64
6	B_{dy}	0.37	0.41	0.45	0.49	0.51
7	B_x/B_{dx}	0.65	0.59	0.54	0.49	0.47
8	B_y/B_{dy}	0.54	0.49	0.44	0.61	0.59
9	$(X)^\beta$	0.63	0.56	0.51	0.46	0.44
10	$(Y)^\beta$	0.51	0.46	0.41	0.58	0.56

columns 1 and 4 and therefore, for this example, this approach requires more steel than that indicated by the method outlined on page 119. This may not be true for all cases.

Slender Columns

Introduction

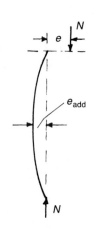

Fig. 5.18
Additional
eccentricity for
slender columns

Slender columns are those for which the slenderness ratio is between 12 and 18 for cantilever elements, and between 12 and 27 for others. Both uniaxial and biaxial bending are treated in a similar manner to that outlined for short columns except that an additional moment due to the slenderness must be included in the calculation. Due to the slenderness there will be an increased eccentricity, e_{add} in Fig. 5.18, which increases the moment arm of the applied vertical load. The additional moment due to this eccentricity is a function of the curvature at the centre of the effective length, and although this varies with material properties and end conditions, a reasonable approximation can be made as to its value. Using this approximation the resulting equation for the additional moment has been expressed[5.5, 5.8] as

$$M_a = N(h_{ef})^2/2000t \qquad [5.23]$$

and this equation can be expressed in non-dimensional form as

$$B_a = L(h_{ef}/t)^2/2000. \qquad [5.24]$$

Uniaxial Bending

In order to design for the general case it would be necessary to work from first principles using the basic assumptions listed (pages 100–102) and designing for the applied axial load and an increased bending moment in accordance with Eq. 5.24.

For doubly reinforced rectangular and symmetrical sections the methods outlined for short columns under uniaxial bending can be used after including the additional moment obtained from Eq. 5.24. It follows therefore that the charts can still be used for this case.

Biaxial Bending

Although for short columns it is possible to treat the biaxial case as if it were uniaxial, this approach is not recommended for slender columns. Account should be taken of the biaxial bending and an allowance made for additional bending due to the increased eccentricity.

The method of design is similar to that shown on biaxial bending and as illustrated on page 118 except that the moments have to be increased to allow for the additional eccentricity. The effective height was not required for the illustrative example shown on page 119 although there was an implicit assumption that the column was short. If, for example, the effective height of the column was changed to 6.44 m then the slenderness ratio would be equal to 14 and the additional moment B_a, from Eq. 5.24, becomes 0.049 and this value would have to be added to either B_x or B_y, depending on the direction of the additional eccentricity, before proceeding with the rest of the calculation shown in the example.

Walls

Walls subjected to combined vertical loading and bending can be designed in a similar manner to that outlined above for columns, as long as there is double reinforcement and the section is symmetrical. Both short and slender walls can, in effect, be treated as columns using the unit length of wall as the width. The charts could be used for all cases following the procedures outlined in the previous sections.

For walls which are singly reinforced the designer would have to work from first principles using the basic assumptions given (pages 100–102). Charts could be drawn for this case in a similar manner to that used to construct the charts for the doubly reinforced case. The same non-dimensional procedure could be used with the omission of the term representing one of the reinforcements.

Deflection and Cracking

Since it is usual to stipulate limiting values of certain dimensions, such as the ratio of span to effective depth, there is no need to make detailed calculations to check the limit states for deflection and cracking, as long as these limitations are adhered to.

In the British code it is suggested that unacceptable cracking due to bending is unlikely to occur if the following condition is true:

$$N > A_m f_k/2 \qquad [5.25]$$

where A_m is the cross-sectional area of the masonry. If the vertical load is less than this then the column should be treated as a beam for the purposes of crack control.

Note that the limiting condition given in Eq. 5.25 can be expressed as

$$L > \gamma_{mm}/2 \qquad [5.26]$$

and, since the usual values of γ_{mm} are 2.0 for the special category of manufacturing control and 2.3 for the normal category of control, Eq. 5.26 suggests that L_d should be above the values 1.0, for special category, and above 1.15 for normal. If the value of L is less, then additional reinforcement to control cracking should be provided. The detailing of this additional reinforcement can be achieved by treating the column as a beam.

References

5.1   British Standards Institution 1985 *British Standard Code of Practice for Use of Masonry. BS 5628:Part 2 Structural Use of Reinforced and Prestressed Masonry* London

5.2   Anderson D E, Hoffman E S 1969 Design of brick masonry columns. In Johnson F B (ed) *Designing, Engineering and Constructing with Masonry Products* Gulf, Houston, Texas pp 94−100

5.3   British Standards Institution 1985 *British Standard Code of Practice. BS 8110 Structural Use of Concrete* London

5.4   British Standards Institution 1972 *Code of Practice for the Structural Use of Concrete CP 110* Nov 1972 London

5.5   Kong F K, Evans R H 1987 *Reinforced and Prestressed Concrete* 3rd edn Van Nostrand Reinhold (UK) London pp 248−91

5.6   Davies S R, El-Traify M W 1984 Influence of biaxial bending on short columns of reinforced masonry. *International Symposium on Reinforced and Prestressed Masonry* University of Edinburgh Aug 1984 pp 234−47

5.7   Davies S R, El-Traify M W 1984 Uniaxial and biaxial bending of reinforced brickwork columns. *Fourth International Brick Masonry Conference* Rome 1984

5.8   Cranston W B 1972 *Analysis and Design of Reinforced Concrete Columns* Research report No 20, Cement and Concrete Association, London

6   Prestressed Masonry Walls

M E Phipps, University of Manchester Institute of
Science and Technology

Introduction

Adding compressive prestress to a masonry wall can improve its load-
carrying performance. This is because although masonry has a relatively
high compressive strength it can only carry quite small tensile stresses.
If sufficient prestress is applied tensile stresses in the masonry can be
eliminated entirely under serviceability conditions and the compressive
strength of the masonry over the whole section can be mobilized.
Compared with plain masonry walls, prestressed walls are thinner and
lighter, deflections are smaller and the walls have improved ability to
cope with large settlements and seismic forces. In prestressed walls,
unlike reinforced walls, cracking need not take place under working
loads.

Types of Prestressed Masonry Wall

There are three basic types of prestressed wall: the solid wall, the cavity
wall and the wall with a geometric cross-section (Fig. 6.1). In all the
systems the post-tensioning method of prestress is used and the tendons
are usually regarded as unbonded. The majority of walls are prestressed
in the vertical direction only, because this is the simplest form of
construction and, for most cases, that is all that is required.

Solid Walls

A solid wall does not have to be made with solid units: perforated or
hollow bricks and blocks may be used as shown in Fig. 6.2. The term
'solid' means that the prestressing tendons or their ducts, if they have
them, are built into the body of the wall as the masonry is laid and they
are fixed firmly in place with mortar or grout. The fixing will not
normally be sufficient to give any structurally reliable bond between the
masonry and the tendons, however. Sometimes the bricks or blocks have
to be cut around the tendons or they may be specially made in the factory.

Fig. 6.1 The three
basic types of
prestressed wall:
(a) solid wall; (b)
cavity wall; (c)
geometric walls

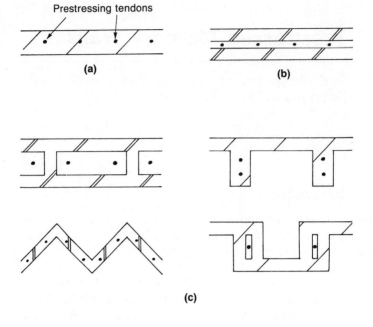

Fig. 6.2 Examples
of solid walls

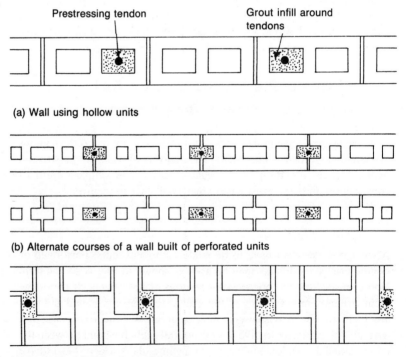

(a) Wall using hollow units

(b) Alternate courses of a wall built of perforated units

(c) Quetta bond wall using solid units

An example of a solid wall at Regensdorf in Switzerland[6.1] is shown in Fig. 6.3.

Fig. 6.3 A 250 mm wide solid wall of calcium silicate bricks at Regensdorf in Switzerland. The wall, which is up to 7.7 m high, is built off a 1 m high in situ reinforced concrete wall which provides the anchorage for the VSL strand system.[6.10]

Cavity Walls

The cavity wall is different from the solid wall in that the tendons are placed in the open cavity between the two leaves (Fig. 6.4(a)). The cavity is not grouted up so the leaves may act independently especially when the wall is subjected to a large load from one side and the wall ties are not strong enough to transfer the load from one leaf to the other. In such a case the structural behaviour is as shown in Fig. 6.4(b). The loaded leaf behaves as a propped cantilever, the prop (which will deflect) being provided by the top of the unloaded leaf acting as a pure cantilever with an end point load. The integrity of the full, or original, section of a cavity wall behaving like this is not therefore maintained under load as is normally expected for structural walls. Notwithstanding this, however, such walls can carry considerable side load as can be seen from Fig. 6.5 which shows a 1.5 m high wall failing at an air bag pressure of over 10 kN m^{-2}. The wall was tested by Witt and Aryamanesh at the University of Manchester Institute of Science and Technology in 1979.

If the cavity is grouted up the cavity wall becomes, in effect, a solid wall. A cavity wall with only one of the leaves prestressed is considered to be a solid wall with a separate masonry veneer cladding.

Fig. 6.4 The cavity wall as a prestressed wall

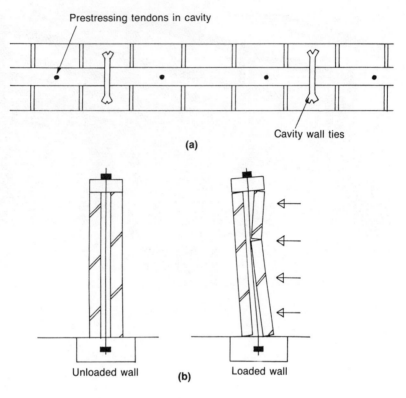

Prestressing tendons in cavity

Cavity wall ties

(a)

Unloaded wall   **(b)**   Loaded wall

Geometric Walls

A wall with a geometric cross-section is one in which the masonry units are laid in such a pattern that the resulting cross-section is not solid and is not necessarily rectangular. Examples are the 'I' and 'T', box and triangular shapes found in diaphragm, piered and chevron walls (Fig. 6.6). A geometric wall can be configured in such a way that it is ideal for vertical prestressing. Preferably, the tendons are placed in open cavities but they may also be built into some part of the masonry as in a solid wall. Figure 6.7 shows a prestressed brickwork diaphragm wall used as a bridge abutment in Cambridgeshire in England. [6.2]

Comparison of Wall Types

Table 6.1 compares the section properties of the three types of vertically prestressed wall made with 100 mm wide units to give approximately the same cross-sectional area per metre. It is assumed in the table that the two leaves of the cavity wall act independently but with equal

Fig. 6.5 Brick
cavity walls 1.5 m
high under test at
UMIST. The clay
bricks, with an
average crushing
strength of
80 N mm^{-2}, were
laid 1:3 plasticized
mortar. High
tensile steel bars
were used as
tendons

contribution to the strength of the wall. To calculate the moment to cause
cracking of the walls the section modulus of each wall has simply been
multiplied by the maximum flexural tensile stress the wall can sustain.
This is assumed to be 0.25 N mm^{-2} for the unprestressed walls and,
with a prestress of 1.5 N mm^{-2}, is 1.75 N mm^{-2} for the prestressed
walls. It can be seen that for approximately the same plan area, and

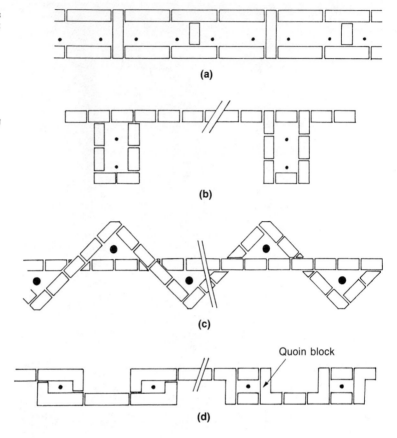

therefore approximately the same amount of masonry, the solid wall is more than twice as effective in resisting bending moments as the cavity wall while the geometric wall is more than eight times as effective. Indeed with a modest level of prestress of only 1.5 N mm^{-2} the prestressed geometric wall has over 60 times the flexural cracking strength of the unprestressed cavity wall while it uses only 15 per cent more masonry.

For linear elastic behaviour, therefore, the important section property from the point of view of effectiveness of prestress is the ratio of the section modulus to the area of the cross-section, i.e. Z/A_m. The higher the value of Z/A_m the greater the potential benefits of prestressing. So for a given amount of masonry the combined effect of improving the geometry of the section and applying prestress can enhance the bending strength of that masonry many times. Of course the assumption of linear elastic behaviour in bending is only applicable to the working load, or serviceability condition. Under ultimate load the wall behaves in a non-linear plastic manner and the bending strength is more directly related to the size of the internal lever arm of the resisting moment, or, approximately, the effective depth of the tendon. For a given wall the greater the effective depth the greater the ultimate bending strength, leading again to the conclusion that the geometric wall is stronger than the other two types.

Because prestressed walls can carry high lateral loads their shear strength must always be checked. Although prestress improves shear strength it is often shear rather than bending which governs load-carrying capacity, especially for geometric walls.

Prestressed Masonry Walls in Use

From the foregoing it can be seen that prestressed walls can be used to advantage to carry heavy loads. Examples are retaining walls, walls to basements, storage silos and water tanks. They can be designed to carry large horizontal point or line loads such as the thrusts from sloping roofs, bridge decks and crane girders. For buildings, prestressing enables cladding walls to be made more slender while prefabricated panels may be factory made. Prestressing can improve a wall's ability to resist large settlements and seismic forces. In such cases the prestress clamps the wall between beams or slabs above and below, the wall becoming the

Fig. 6.7 (a) A 6 m high prestressed diaphragm wall bridge abutment on the Glinton–Northborough bypass, Cambridge, England. Armitage bricks with crushing strengths of 80 and 100 N mm^{-2} were used in conjunction with Macalloy prestressing bars of 32, 40 and 50 mm diameter.

Fig. 6.7 (b) Detail
showing the
diaphragm wall
construction and
the applied
waterproofing to
the tendons

web of a deep storey-height composite girder. The advantages of prestressing can be equally useful for very simple structures such as slender free-standing boundary walls.

The important advantages of economy of material, reduced deflection and elimination of cracks under working loads which prestress brings to a wall are all apparent at the design stage. The other main improvement in performance, ductility, is not so amenable to calculation and is therefore not so obvious.

Table 6.1 Properties of cavity, solid and geometric walls

Type of wall	A_m Plan area $(m^2\ m^{-1} \times 10^{-3})$	Z Section modulus $(m^3\ m^{-1} \times 10^{-3})$	Cracking moment $(kN\ m\ m^{-1})$*		$Z/A_m \times 10^3$
			Prestress $= 0$	Prestress $= 1.5$ $N\ mm^{-2}$	
Cavity† (100/100)	200	3.3	0.8	5.8	17
Solid (215)	215	7.7	1.9	13.5	36
Geometric (440)	233	27.7	6.9	48.5	118

* Flexural tensile stress $= 0.25\ N\ mm^{-2}$.
† Each leaf assumed to act independently.

The ductility is provided in two ways, each being associated with a particular load stage. First, at the working load stage, a prestressed wall exhibits ductile behaviour because it does not suffer from the brittleness of tensile cracking. Second, if the wall is accidently overloaded and cracks are formed the prestressing tendons provide the wall with a ductile tensile component similar to that of reinforcement in a reinforced wall. This second-stage ductility is superior to that of the reinforced wall, however, because once the overload is removed the cracks close up and stage one type ductility returns.

As discussed in Chapter 4, stressing masonry with steel tendons results in a loss of prestress with time due to long-term movements in the masonry and steel and, possibly, slip of the tendon anchorages. This loss, which necessarily results in a loss of wall strength, can only be allowed for if suitable materials are chosen and if there is a knowledge of the way those materials, when under stress, behave with time.

In some cases the prestress may only be required during construction, either for temporary works or where it is to be replaced later by permanent vertical loads from walls above. In other cases the level of prestress may need adjusting over the lifetime of the wall to cater for new loadings.

As with all masonry, prestressed walls must be designed to accommodate other time-related movements as well as those which result in prestress loss. For example, changes in temperature and moisture content can cause longitudinal strains in a wall which must be accommodated with suitable joints.

Construction

A prestressed masonry wall is built off some kind of foundation which may be an *in situ* concrete strip footing, a beam or a slab. It is usually capped by an independent reinforced concrete strip beam (but steel beams have been used) or the edge of a suspended reinforced concrete floor slab. Tendons anchored in the foundation and capping beam, or slab, apply post-tensioned prestress to the wall.

Suitable Masonry

While it is possible to prestress masonry walls built with units and mortar of any type, because of the need to restrict the loss of prestress with time to a minimum it will normally be necessary to use dense aggregate concrete blocks with a minimum crushing strength of 7 N mm^{-2} or bricks with a minimum crushing strength of 20 N mm^{-2} and at least a 1:1:6 (cement:lime:sand) mortar. Losses may not of course be a serious problem where the prestress is only required in the short term when weaker materials could be used.

Masonry Bonding Patterns

To produce a prestressed wall the units may be arranged in a number of different patterns as shown in Figs 6.2, 6.4 and 6.6. In addition, metal ties may be used to bond different sections of the wall together as shown in Fig. 6.8. Metal ties are particularly useful where a painted-on damp-proof membrane is to be incorporated at the vertical joint between, say, the ribs and the leaves of a wall.

Geometric walls in particular can have many attractive profiles. The bonding patterns can be arranged with some panels recessed or protruding or ribs may project through the face to improve appearance (see Fig. 6.9).

Fig. 6.8 Metal ties used to bond walls: (a) long ties across a narrow diaphragm wall showing alternate courses. Ties should not be bedded across a perpend joint in the leaves; (b) short ties across a wide diaphragm wall showing stretcher bond on each leaf with staggered joints

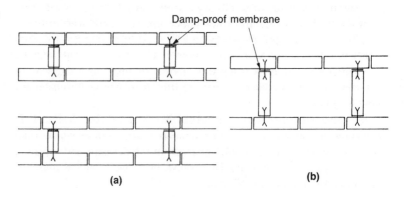

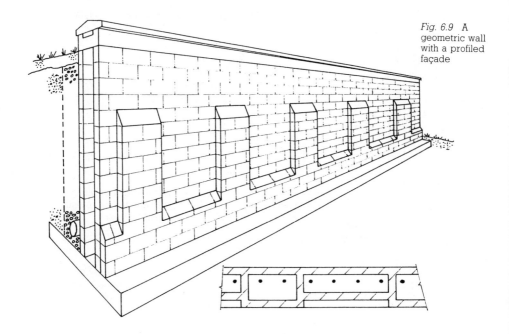

Fig. 6.9 A geometric wall with a profiled façade

Tendons

High-tensile steel tendons suitable for post-tensioning are necessary because the highest possible initial steel strain (and therefore the highest possible steel stress) is required to offset losses of prestress due to creep and shrinkage of the masonry. For ease of construction, bars such as the Macalloy prestressing bars shown in Fig. 6.10 are preferable to loose strands or wires because they are sufficiently stiff to stand vertically without lateral support and short (or long) lengths can be screwed together remotely; but VSL International has developed a system which avoids the problem of the flexibility of strands by placing them in galvanized steel ducts as shown in Fig. 6.11.

Placing the tendons in cavities or voids in the masonry is the simplest, and therefore the most economical, way to build a prestressed wall. With bar tendons short starter bars with threaded couplers are cast into the foundation at the correct positions (they may be eccentric or concentric) and the masonry is then built around them to the desired height. Short lengths of tendon are then screwed into place as the wall is built or long lengths are screwed in from the top of the wall. After the capping beams have been put in place and the wall has gained sufficient strength the bars are tensioned up with a portable hydraulic jack. If strands in steel

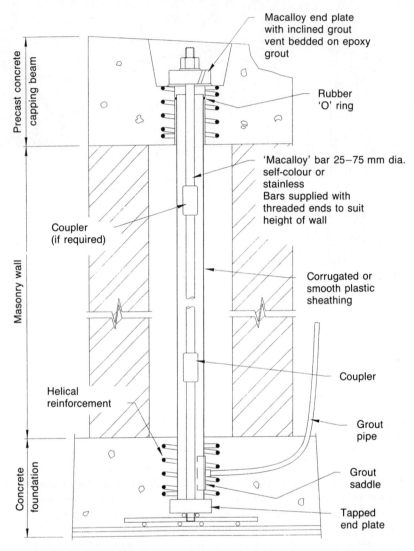

Macalloy end plate
with inclined grout
vent bedded on epoxy
grout

Rubber
'O' ring

'Macalloy' bar 25–75 mm dia.
self-colour or
stainless
Bars supplied with
threaded ends to suit
height of wall

Precast concrete
capping beam

Coupler
(if required)

Masonry wall

Corrugated or
smooth plastic
sheathing

Coupler

Helical
reinforcement

Grout
pipe

Concrete
foundation

Grout
saddle

Tapped
end plate

Fig. 6.10 The
Macalloy high
tensile steel bar
post-tensioning
system of McCalls
Special Products,
England

ducts are used self-activating dead end anchorages are first cast in the
foundation and short pieces of duct are threaded first to the anchorages
and then on to each other until the top of the wall is reached when the
precast concrete capping beams are put in place. When the wall is strong
enough the strands are then passed down the tubes into the dead end
anchorages and stressed. Figures 6.12 and 6.13 show two typical
installations.

   With a wall constructed in this way the tendons are unbonded and
anchored to the wall only at the bottom, through the foundation, and

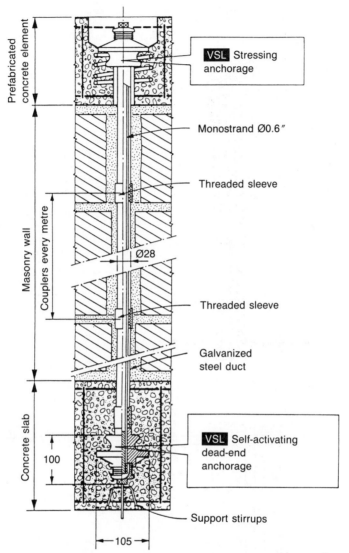

Fig. 6.11 The wire
strand post-
tensioning system
of VSL
International,
Switzerland

at the top, through the capping beams. If the tendons are in large cavities
they may be restrained in position up the height of the wall by headers
protruding into the cavities, as in Fig. 6.12, but this will only normally
be necessary for very tall walls.

Foundations

Prestressed walls must spring from and be firmly anchored to
foundations. These will commonly be similar to those needed for

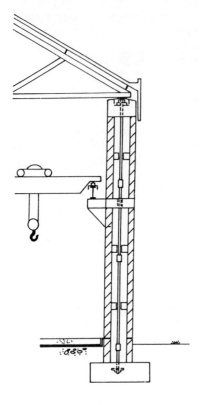

Fig. 6.12 A prestressed blockwork wall to a tall industrial building

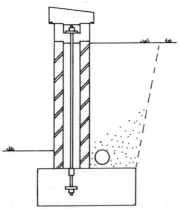

Fig. 6.13 A prestressed brickwork retaining wall

reinforced concrete walls except that, instead of projecting reinforcing bars, anchorages for the prestressing tendons are cast in. The anchorages may project above the surface of the foundation or they may finish flush with the surface, as shown in Figs 6.12 and 6.13. The foundations must be designed for the loads acting upon them and if they sit directly on the ground, as they would for retaining walls, due regard must be paid to the strength of the soil and the possibility of overturning and sliding. Sometimes the foundation may become part of the wall itself, such as the case shown in Fig. 6.3 where the masonry sits on a 1 m high, *in situ* reinforced concrete wall.

Capping Beams

All prestressed masonry walls will need some form of anchorage at the top for the prestressing tendons. If the wall is free-standing the anchorage will most likely take the form of a series of precast reinforced concrete beams laid end to end over the whole length of the wall, but *in situ* capping beams have also been used in this circumstance (Fig. 6.7). Where an *in situ* reinforced concrete floor slab rests on the top of, say, a basement wall this can be used as the anchorage medium. Neill[6.3] used the steel edge beams of the roof to anchor the cavity wall tendons for the cladding panels of a factory building.

Test Evidence

There is now a considerable body of test evidence on the performance of prestressed masonry walls and also on prestressed masonry beams of similar construction with unbonded tendons. The results from beam tests are just as useful as those from wall tests because a wall may be regarded as a series of vertical, interconnected beams built side by side.

Wall Tests

One of the earliest tests on prestressed masonry was carried out by Rosenhaupt, Beresford and Blakey in Australia in 1967.[6.4] They tested a 2.4 m high by 10.0 m long concrete blockwork wall which was post-tensioned between a reinforced concrete floor beam at the top and a reinforced concrete foundation beam at the bottom. The experiment showed that such a wall, acting as a deep beam, could accommodate large ground movements. Some 15 years later, Curtin tested two prestressed brickwork diaphragm walls which were 7.6 m high by 7.6 m long by 0.45 m overall width.[6.5, 6.6] Between them, they were subjected to seven different levels of axial prestress and at each level of prestress a uniform lateral load was applied up to a serviceability limit. To simulate the roof reaction in a building, the walls were propped at the top so that under test they acted like propped cantilevers. The maximum test loads ranged from 2.3 to 7.2 kN m^{-2} with corresponding prestress levels ranging from 0.30 to 1.38 Nmm^{-2} respectively. The characteristic strength of the masonry in these tests was 11.0 N mm^{-2}.

To enable higher levels of prestress to be applied, Curtin and Howard followed up these tests with three test walls built of brickwork with a characteristic strength greater than 35 N m^{-2}.[6.7] The walls were 6 m high, free cantilevers and 3.4 m long, again with a diaphragm cross-section, the overall width in these cases being 557 mm. An approximately triangular load distribution was created with six air bags to represent earth loading and with prestress levels up to 8.35 N mm^{-2}, Curtin obtained a side load pressure at the base up to 82.8 kN m^{-2}. Other tests on prestressed brickwork retaining walls have been carried out by Ambrose, Hulse and Mohajery, and Hobbs and Daou, Hobbs' work being at model scale.[6.8, 6.9] To examine the effects of a large thrust at the top of a wall in addition to earth pressure, Garrity and Garwood have successfully tested a full-sized bridge abutment in prestressed high-strength brickwork.[6.10]

Montague built four concrete blockwork diaphragm walls, two of which were 3.0 m high by 3.0 m long and prestressed.[6.11] One wall, wall 1, was 550 mm wide with eccentric prestress and the other, wall 2, was 440 mm wide with concentric prestress. The walls were tested to failure as free-standing cantilevers under uniform lateral pressure. Wall 1 with a prestress level of 2.14 N mm^{-2} on the loaded face and 1.12 N mm^{-2} on the unloaded face failed in shear due to diagonal cracks in the webs at a maximum side pressure of 19.8 kN m^{-2}. The formation of the shear cracks was first observed at a side load of 11.8 kN m^{-2}. Wall 2, prestressed to 1.98 N mm^{-2}, also failed in shear at a side pressure of 11.1 kN m^{-2}, the cracks first being seen at a load of 3.3 kN m^{-2}.

All of the tests described above have been on walls with prestress in the vertical direction only. In parallel with those developments Huizer *et al.* have conducted a series of tests on prestressed walls with both horizontal and vertical prestress.[6.12, 6.13] They have shown that substantial increases in the racking shear strength of masonry walls can be achieved by prestressing in both directions.

Beam Tests

In the broad sense beam tests can be divided into two types: those that have been carried out with the intention of finding out the properties of beams *per se* and those that have been conducted to discover some property related to the performance of walls. Only the second type of test is mentioned here, the first type being the subject of Chapter 4.

All the beams in this second group of tests had geometric cross-sections with post-tensioned, unbonded tendons in large voids so they relate to the behaviour of geometric walls. The brick box beams of Williams and the concrete blockwork ones of Montague help formulate design rules on ultimate flexural strength, while the blockwork 'I'-beams of Montague and the brickwork 'I'- and 'T'-beams of Roumani give information on shear strength.[6.14–6.16] Lokkas looked at the strength of brickwork beams with diamond-shaped cross-sections which were devised to simulate zigzag or chevron walls.[6.17]

Design Method

Design guidance for prestressed masonry is available in the publications of the Aggregate Concrete Block Association[6.18] and the Brick Development Association.[6.19] In the UK methods for design have been codified, first by the British Ceramic Research Association in its SP-91 publication[6.20] and then by the British Standards Institution in BS 5628:Part 2:1985.[6.21]

It is preferable to use the limit state design method for prestressed masonry walls. The aim of this design method is that the walls will not become unfit for their purpose by collapsing, overturning or buckling (ultimate limit states), by having deflections that are too great or cracks that are too wide (serviceability limit states) and that they will be durable over their intended design life.

Ultimate Limit State

The whole structure, of which the wall may only be part, must be designed to transmit safely all the dead, wind and imposed loads to the foundations. This will mean that, for instance, if the floor of a building is used as a horizontal prop to the top of a prestressed basement wall then, as well as ensuring that the wall itself will not rupture or buckle, the floor and its connections to the top of the wall must be strong enough and stiff enough to carry any horizontal loads involved. Similarly when a prestressed wall is used to retain earth the reinforced concrete foundation must be designed to act integrally with the wall.

Serviceability Limit State

Deflection is unlikely to be a problem with a prestressed wall because the allowable serviceability load stresses can be chosen to satisfy any likely limiting deflection criterion (deflections measured in the laboratory on full-scale walls at loads that cause flexural cracking are less than 1/750 of the span).

Cracking in prestressed masonry walls can take three forms: spalling due to flexural compression, flexural tensile cracking and tensile cracking due to the combined action of bending and shear. Spalling is a failure criterion that must be considered in prestressed walls. Flexural tensile cracking can be controlled and is best eliminated. Cracking in the webs should always be prevented.

Durability

The masonry units and mortar must be of sufficient quality to ensure that the walls do not deteriorate due to environmental conditions. If wall ties are used they should always be corrosion resistant. Workmanship, curing and quality control in the manufacturing plant and on site have great influence on the durability of all masonry structures. For detailed provisions on durability reference should be made to the appropriate standards and authorities in the country concerned.

Corrosion of the prestressing tendons must be prevented. Corrosion-resistant tendons such as stainless high-tensile steel bars can be used or ordinary high-tensile steel bars can be protected with an applied corrosion-resistant coating or sheath. When strands in galvanized steel ducts are used the strands themselves are usually double protected with grease and plastic sheathing. It is important to note that the masonry is unlikely to provide protection against corrosion if the tendons are simply built into the solid parts of the wall. From the corrosion point of view, as well as for ease of construction therefore, it is preferable to place the tendons in cavities or voids in the wall and it is a good idea to make provision for inspection of the tendons if there is any likelihood of corrosion in service (with threaded bars or strands in ducts it is possible to replace any defective tendons).

Strength of Prestressed Masonry Walls

This section is mainly confined to the strength of walls prestressed in the vertical direction only and subjected to lateral load. When prestress in the horizontal direction is added the same principles of analysis and design hold. Guidance on the combined use of horizontal and vertical prestress for in-plane loading may be found in the work of Huizer.[6.12, 6.13]

The safety factors and levels of stress suggested below are based on British practice and should be satisfactory elsewhere. The text makes it clear where these have been applied so that alternative ones can be inserted if desired.

A Prestressed Wall under Load

A prestressed wall will commonly be used to carry high horizontal loads, such as the earth on a retaining wall, but there may sometimes be significant vertical load as well from, say, the floors and walls above a basement. Resistance to horizontal load is provided by the bending and shear strengths of the wall and any vertical, or axial, load is allowed for in combination with the applied prestress.

The strength of a wall depends upon the configuration of the cross-section, the properties of the masonry, the axial loads applied to the wall (including self-weight) and upon the level of prestress applied. A prestressed wall does not behave in the same way as an unprestressed, or plain, wall carrying axial compressive load from above. Although the direction of compressive prestress force is the same as that of any applied compressive axial load (and they may therefore appear to have the same effect) the provision of tendons in the section to apply the prestress causes a prestressed wall to behave differently at ultimate in bending because the tendons give the wall's internal resisting moment a tensile component which is not present in an unprestressed wall.

Similarly the presence of prestress affects the mode of failure in shear; the high compressive axial load associated with prestress causes shear failure to occur in the masonry units and the mortar joints and not just in the joints as is the case for plain walls.

There will be a loss of prestress with time and an estimate of the amount of loss must be made before the long-term strength of a wall can be determined.

Bending Strength

A prestressed wall should be designed for the serviceability condition and then its ultimate moment capacity should be checked.

Bending Strength at Serviceability Load

There are two cases of serviceability load which need to be examined: at transfer of prestress and under the working loads after losses.

The loads and forces involved must not cause cracking on the tension side (nominally the back face) or overstressing on the compression side (nominally the front face). To this end the compression stress is limited to one-third of the characteristic strength of the masonry, f_k, under the design loads and to $0.4f_{kt}$ at transfer, where f_{kt} is the strength of the masonry at transfer. Tension stress is not allowed in either case since the characteristic flexural tensile strength of masonry, f_{kx}, will usually be much smaller (as well as less reliable) than the effective prestress.

The partial safety factor for load, γ_f, is taken as 1.0 at transfer and under the design loads. The material partial safety factors, γ_m, are, in effect, replaced by the compression and tension stress limitations for the masonry, and for the tendons by limiting the jacking force to 70 per cent of their characteristic breaking load.

For the purposes of the next two sections, we assume a linear elastic distribution of stress and referring to Fig. 6.14.

Fig. 6.14
Serviceability
stresses

Front face

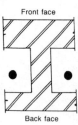

Back face

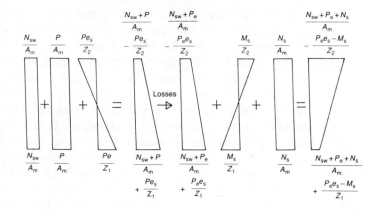

At transfer

$$f_{2t} = (N_{sw}+P)/A_m - Pe_s/Z_2 \qquad [6.1]$$

$$f_{1t} = (N_{sw}+P)/A_m + Pe_s/Z_1 \qquad [6.2]$$

where f_{2t} = front face stress at transfer;
f_{1t} = back face stress at transfer;
N_{sw} = self-weight;
P = prestress force;
A_m = cross-sectional area of masonry;
Z_2 = section modulus for front face;
Z_1 = section modulus for back face;
e_s = eccentricity of prestress.

Under working loads   After losses the applied prestressing force
at transfer, P, becomes the effective prestressing force, P_e. P_e does not
significantly change with variations in working load and so with the
addition of the applied serviceability moment, M_s, and the applied
serviceability axial load, N_s, Eqs 6.1 and 6.2 become

$$f_{2s} = (N_{sw}+P_e+N_s)/A_m - (P_e e - M_s)/Z_2 \qquad [6.3]$$

$$f_{1s} = (N_{sw}+P_e+N_s)/A_m + (P_e e - M_s)/Z_1 \qquad [6.4]$$

where f_{2s} = front face stress at serviceability load;
f_{1s} = back face stress at serviceability load.

There may be an intermediate stage where M_s is applied (from, say,
backfill) and the walls above are built to give N_s later. If the permanent
part of N_s is sufficiently high P_e may be allowed to fall off to zero with
time.

Note: In Eqs 6.1—6.4 free cantilever action with the back face being
the loaded face is assumed in assigning the notation to the stresses, i.e.

$$f_{2t} > 0$$
$$f_{1t} < 0.4f_{kt}$$
$$f_{2s} < 0.33f_k$$
$$f_{1s} > 0$$

Bending Strength at Ultimate Load

At ultimate, cracking of the masonry on the tension side causes the tendon stress to increase beyond P_e. The allowable tendon stresses are so chosen, however, that, for the ultimate moment, failure will be the result of crushing of the masonry rather than steel fracture. The distribution of stress over the compression zone is assumed to be uniform, and the masonry is assumed to have no strength in tension. It is further assumed that for sections with webs and flanges the webs do not contribute to bending strength. For such cases it also follows that the maximum depth of the compression zone cannot be greater than the flange thickness. Thus from Fig. 6.15(a), resolving along the axis of the wall:

$$(f_k/\gamma_{mm})\ Bx\ =\ A_{ps}(f_{pb}/\gamma_{ms})$$

so $x_1\ =\ R(f_s/f_e)$ [6.5]

where x_1 $= x/d$;
         R $= (A_{ps}/Bd)\ (f_e/f_k)\ (\gamma_{mm}/\gamma_{ms})$;
         x $=$ depth to neutral axis $\leq$ flange thickness;
         d $=$ effective depth of tendon;
         f_k $=$ characteristic compressive strength of masonry;
         B $=$ breadth of masonry in compression;
         A_{ps} $=$ area of tendon;
         f_e $=$ effective prestress in tendon;
         f_{pb} $=$ stress in tendon at ultimate.

Taking moments about the centre line of the tendon, the ultimate moment, M_u, is

$$M_u\ =\ (f_k/\gamma_{mm})Bx(d-x/2).$$ [6.6]

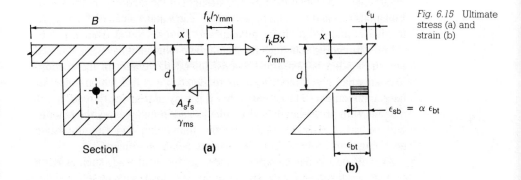

Fig. 6.15 Ultimate stress (a) and strain (b)

The distribution of strain across the masonry section is assumed to be linear, as shown in Fig. 6.15(b). Because the tendon is not bonded to the masonry, the tendon strain due to bending, ϵ_{sb}, is not the same as the masonry strain due to bending at the same level, ϵ_{bt}, but is some other value:

$$\epsilon_{sb} = \alpha \epsilon_{bt}$$

where α is a bond factor.

From Fig. 6.15(b):

$$x/d = \epsilon_u/(\epsilon_{sb} + \epsilon_u)$$

where ϵ_u is the ultimate masonry compression strain. So

$$x_1 = \alpha \epsilon_u/(\epsilon_{pb} + \alpha \epsilon_u).$$

ϵ_{sb} is the tendon strain due to bending only and the stress associated with this strain is f_{sb}, the tendon stress due to bending. Therefore, providing f_{sb} is within the linear elastic range of the tendon,

$$x_1 = E_s \, \alpha \epsilon_u/(f_{sb} + E_s \, \alpha \epsilon_u) \qquad [6.7]$$

where E_s is Young's modulus for the tendon. A common value for ϵ_u is 0.0035 and a suitable value for α is 0.05.

The total stress in the tendon at ultimate, f_{pb}, is equal to the sum of the effective prestress, f_e, and the stress due to bending, i.e.

$$f_{pb} = f_e + f_{sb}$$

or

$$f_{pb}/f_e = 1 + f_{sb}/f_e$$

and substituting for f_{sb} in Eq. 6.7 gives

$$x_1 = L/\{(f_{pb}/f_e) - 1 + L\} \qquad [6.8]$$

where $L = E_s \, \alpha \epsilon_u/f_e$.

Here f_{pb}/f_e will always be greater than 1.0 but it should not be taken higher than 1.5 so that the ultimate strength of the tendon is not reached. Equations 6.5 and 6.8 can be solved for particular values of f_e and f_{pb}/f_e to give x_1 and the ultimate moment can then be found from Eq. 6.6.

In the foregoing equations for the ultimate moment it has been assumed that the tendon is restrained against lateral movement in the section. Williams has given modifications to Eqs 6.6 and 6.8 which cater for lateral movement in large voids, but it is easy in practice to restrain the tendons with projecting bricks or blocks and in many cases the tendons will be sufficiently restrained by the foundation and capping beam anchorages to prevent such movements being significant.[6.14]

At ultimate the partial safety factor, γ_f, for dead load, such as earth or water, is taken as 1.4 except when the dead load, such as self-weight, is contributing to the strength of the wall when $\gamma_f = 0.9$. The imposed load partial safety factor is taken to be 1.6. The material partial safety factors are $\gamma_{mm} = 2.0$ (assuming special category of manufacturing control) for masonry and $\gamma_{ms} = 1.15$ for steel tendons.

Shear Strength

For a wall built with full masonry bonding shear failure is associated with some form of masonry cracking while for a wall which uses metal ties for bonding the shear force can cause the ties to fail in bending before cracking occurs. Both kinds of failure are considered to be ultimate failure modes so the partial safety factors given above are appropriate.

Shear reinforcement, other than metal wall ties to bind the different parts of the wall together, should not be used if the stress levels are exceeded. In such circumstances the section should be increased in size.

In the following, cracking and tie failure are treated separately.

Shear Cracking

There are two types of shear cracking, mortar joint cracking and diagonal cracking, but mortar joint cracking is usually only associated with unprestressed walls whereas diagonal cracking, i.e. cracking that can pass through the masonry units as well as the mortar joints, is something that happens to prestressed walls.

Some sections, such as a diaphragm wall, have clearly defined webs which will carry the bulk of the shear force and so in the following the width of the section resisting shear is given the term t_w, the 'w' standing for web. For solid, or near solid walls, t_w simply becomes a unit length of the wall.

The distribution of shear stress, v, across the width t_w may be assumed to be evenly distributed over its depth, D, as shown in Fig. 6.16. Therefore

$$V = vDt_w \qquad\qquad [6.9]$$

where V = applied shear force;
       t_w = thickness of wall resisting shear.

High compressive axial loads from prestress strengthen the joints, particularly the horizontal ones, to such an extent that the tensile strength of the units can be weaker than the cracking strength of the joints. Cracks commonly start in the vertical joints and spread diagonally into the units above and below in such cases. Alternatively the cracks move around strong units in a generally diagonal direction. Failure is due to the principal tensile stresses reaching the diagonal tensile strength of the masonry (for simplicity, the critical section is assumed to be at the centroid). There are two cases that have to be considered; the first, (case a), is when the

Fig. 6.16 Shear
stress distribution

$$v = \frac{V}{Dt_w}$$

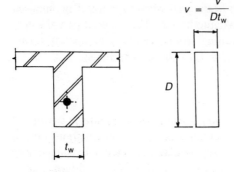

diagonal crack forms in a wall that is uncracked in flexure and the second,
(case b), is when the diagonal crack forms in a wall that has already
suffered flexural cracking.

Case (a)   For a prestressed wall that is not already cracked in
flexure, if it is assumed that the shear stress is uniform across the width
of the cross-section and the shear stress does not affect the distribution
of bending stress then the diagonal cracking strength, V_c, can be
represented by the linear elastic equation

$$V_c = v_c D t_w \qquad\qquad\qquad [6.10]$$

where $v_c = \{(f_t/\gamma_m)^2 + \gamma_f f_p(f_t/\gamma_m)\}^{0.5}$;
        = design shear stress for a wall uncracked in flexure;
    f_t = diagonal tensile strength of masonry;
    f_p = stress due to prestress at the centroid of the section.

In principle, as demonstrated by Ganz,[6.23] the diagonal tensile
strength of masonry may be determined by using a suitable failure theory
if the two compressive strengths of the masonry perpendicular to and
parallel to the bed joints are known. Such failure theories have usually
been based to some extent on tests on shear walls and panels of masonry
with simple unrestrained edge conditions subjected to in-plane forces.
They are not necessarily therefore directly applicable to prestressed walls
which are laterally loaded but the level of stress predicted is of the correct
order of magnitude. For instance, Page, Samarasinghe and Hendry give
the diagonal tensile strength of brick shear walls as[6.23]

$$f_t = 0.7e^{-0.14f_c} - 1.34\theta/\pi - 0.02 \qquad\qquad [6.11a]$$

where f_c = principal compressive stress on the masonry;
        θ = angle of inclination of f_t to the bed joints.

Shear stresses in solid and cavity walls subjected to lateral loads are
usually small but geometric walls rely for their strength on webs which

are in a similar condition to the shear walls described above. The particular geometry of webs is commonly different from large panel shear walls, however, in that webs can be quite short (perhaps only the length of one brick) and, relatively, very tall (the full height of the wall) and their ends are fully fixed into the flanges of the section. In such conditions, for instance, low moment/shear ratios (M/VD) artificially enhance f_t while an increase in D tends to reduce it. If the effects of these are known they can be allowed for. For example, for the webs of diaphragm walls built of solid dense aggregate concrete blocks with a crushing strength of 10 N mm^{-2} in a 1:1:6 mortar Montague found that[6.11]

$$f_t = 1.3 - 0.275M/VD \text{ (N mm}^{-2}) \qquad [6.11b]$$

with maximum $f_t = 0.75$ N mm^{-2}, and minimum $f_t = 0.20$ N mm^{-2}.

Similarly for 'I'-beams built of 25 N mm^{-2} clay bricks on 1:1:6 mortar, Roumani found that f_t may be taken as[6.16]

$$f_t = (74/D) \exp[2.24/(M/VD)] \text{ (N mm}^{-2}) \qquad [6.11c]$$

with maximum $f_t = 1.60$ N mm^{-2}.

Case (b)   When a wall is already cracked in flexure the post-flexural cracking behaviour is essentially that of a tied arch as shown in Fig. 6.17. From Fig. 6.17 the applied moment, M, is given by

$$M = Pd$$

where P = prestress force;
         d = effective tendon depth.

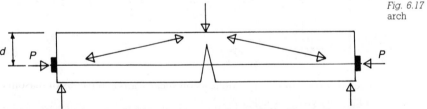

Fig. 6.17 Tied arch

Strictly, the effective tendon depth, d, in the above equation should be replaced by the lever arm of the internal resisting moment but, for a wall, the depth of the compression zone is so small that d is sufficiently accurate.

The moment causing flexural cracking may be taken as M_s (given by Eq. 6.4 with $f_b = 0$) and the prestress force at that moment is P_e so for $M > M_s$

$$M = M_s + d(P - P_e).$$

At the onset of diagonal cracking M becomes the diagonal cracking moment for the wall cracked in flexure, M_{cr}, and P becomes the force in the tendon, P_{cr}, at the moment M_{cr}, i.e.

$$M_{cr} = M_s + d(P_{cr} - P_e).$$ [6.12]

This is shown graphically in Fig. 6.18. If it is now assumed that, after flexural cracking, the tied arch still behaves in a linear elastic manner and that the magnitude and the distribution of stress at the critical position where the diagonal crack will form (assumed to be at the centroid) are the same as that given by linear elastic beam theory, then Eq. 6.10 holds, in the following modified form, for the shear force to give diagonal cracking, V_{cr}:

$$V_{cr} = v_{cr}Dt_w$$ [6.13]

where $v_{cr} = \{(f_t/\gamma_m)^2 + \gamma_f f_{cr}(f_t/\gamma_m)\}^{0.5}$
        $=$ permissible shear stress for wall cracked in flexure,
where $f_{cr} = P_{cr}/A_m =$ prestress at the centroid of the secton at the diagonal cracking load.

P_{cr} must be greater than P_e for Eq. 6.12 to hold but it must not be taken as greater than 70 per cent of the characteristic tendon strength, i.e. $0.7 A_s f_{pu}$. Also V_{cr} cannot be greater than the shear force associated with the ultimate failure moment, M_u, of Eq. 6.6.

Fig. 6.18
Moment–prestress force relation for a wall cracked in flexure

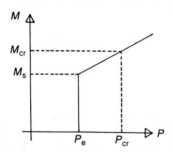

M_{cr} and V_{cr} are related by the loading system and the constraints on the wall: for example, for a free cantilever retaining wall of height h, subjected to a triangularly distributed load, $M_{cr} = V_{cr}h/3$. Equations 6.11(a), (b) or (c) give a value for f_t so Eqs 6.12 and 6.13 can be solved for the two unknowns V_{cr} and P_{cr}.

Alternatively, Eq. 6.12 can be converted to stress form for a particular type of wall. For example, for the cantilever wall mentioned, M_s and V_s are related in the same way as M_{cr} and V_{cr}. Since $V = vDt_w$:

$$M_{cr} = v_{cr}(hDt_w/3) \quad \text{and} \quad M_s = v_s(hDt_w).$$

$P_e = f_p A_m$ and $P_{cr} = f_{cr}A_m$ so Eq. 6.12 becomes, for a free cantilever wall with a triangular distribution of load,

$$v_{cr} = v_s + S(f_{cr} + f_p) \qquad [6.12a]$$

where $S = (3dA_m)/(hDt_w)$.

Wall Tie Failure

If the integrity of the section is maintained by metal wall ties the ties must be designed to transfer the shear stresses from one part of the section to the other in the manner of shear connectors.

Figure 6.19 shows a cross-section through a wall in which the flanges are connected to the webs with ties. The shear force, V_t, acting on an individual tie is

$$V_t = t_w vs \qquad [6.14]$$

where s = tie spacing.

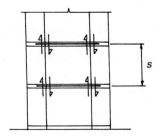

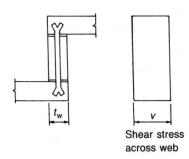

Fig. 6.19 Shear on wall ties

Shear stress across web

It is assumed in Eq. 6.14 that the ties transfer all the shear force across the interface between the parts of the section. Any shear strength which the vertical mortar joint may possess should be ignored especially if a damp-proof membrane is provided. The shear stress, v, is assumed to be that given by Eq. 6.9. The tie carries the shear force across the joint in bending as illustrated in Fig. 6.20(a), deforming elastically until two plastic hinges are formed a distance j apart (Fig. 6.20(b)). The applied moment, m, causing the hinges to form is thus, from Fig. 6.20(b),

Fig. 6.20 Plastic
hinges in a tie

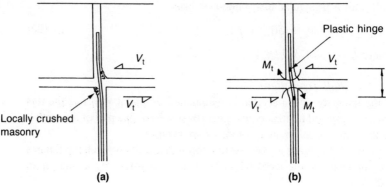

Locally crushed
masonry

Plastic hinge

(a)   (b)

$$m = V_t j.$$

Experiments have shown that the distance, j, may be taken as six times
the tie thickness, t.

A tie of width r, thickness t and yield strength f_y has a plastic moment
of resistance, $m_t = f_y r t^2/4$. At failure the applied moment is resisted
by two plastic hinges:

$$m = 2m_t$$

so

$$V_t = f_y r t^2/2j$$

or

$$V_t = f_y K_v \qquad\qquad [6.15]$$

where $K_v = (rt^2)/(2j)$, the tie coefficient.

Combining Eqs 6.14 and 6.15, the required K_v is

$$K_v = t_w vs/f_y$$

or, with the partial safety factor for steel strength, γ_{ms}, built in:

$$K_v = t_w vs\, \gamma_{ms}/f_y \qquad\qquad [6.16]$$

Vertical Damp-proof Membrane

If a vertical damp-proof membrane is required in a wall this will not
be detrimental to the strength of the wall providing ties are put in the
wall according to the rules given above. The vertical joint containing
the damp-proof membrane must be filled with mortar to develop the full
strength of the ties. The best kind of membrane in these circumstances
is one of the painted-on types.

Horizontal Bending of Flanges

Certain walls such as walls with piers and diaphragm walls have very definite flanges which may have to carry the applied loads in horizontal bending to the piers or webs of the section. The design is based on the flexural tensile strength of the masonry and is carried out at the serviceability limit state only, for the following reasons:

(a) The flexural tensile strength of the masonry in the horizontal direction is reliable because the vertical mortar joints are staggered and the units are interlocking. Furthermore it is enhanced by vertical prestress.
(b) Failure by vertical cracking cannot be tolerated because, unlike bed-joint cracking, the cracks will not close up on unloading.
(c) For webs spaced up to 13.5 times the thickness of the flanges the post-cracking ultimate bending strength in this direction is higher than the cracking strength because of internal arching, so designing for the serviceability moment automatically satisfies ultimate strength.

For a linear elastic stress distribution the horizontal resisting moment, M_h, is

$$M_h = fz$$

where z = section modulus for flange in horizontal bending;
f = bending stress.

Since the flange is continuous over supports at equal distances, B, apart the applied bending moment for a uniformly distributed load, w, can be assumed to be

$$M = wB^2/10.$$

The maximum value of B for this condition is therefore

$$B = (10fz/w)^{0.5} \tag{6.17}$$

with

$$z = t_f^2/6 \text{ per unit height of wall}$$

where t_f is the flange thickness.

The limiting value for f is f_b, the bending strength of prestressed masonry perpendicular to the bed joints. The application of vertical prestress increases the horizontal flexural strength of masonry beyond the normal characteristic strength perpendicular to the bed joints, f_{kx}.[6.24] The effect can be seen as a clamping action which, through friction, increases the torsional shear resistance of the bed joints.[6.25] f_b can be assumed to increase in direct proportion to the increase in prestress from a base level of f_{kx}, i.e.

$$f_b = f_{kx} + Kf_{ps}$$

where f_{ps} = net vertical prestress on the leaf;
         K = constant.

f_{ps} is calculated as the compression stress on the loaded leaf under working loads. In most cases, therefore, f_{ps} will be equal to f_{1s} in Eq. 6.4. K may be taken as 0.4 and if the serviceability safety factors of 1.5 for the masonry and 0.9 for the prestress force are applied to f_{kx} and f_{ps} respectively f_b becomes f_{kb}, the design bending strength of the prestressed masonry perpendicular to the bed joint i.e.[6.24]

$$f_{kb} = 0.67f_{kx} + 0.36f_{ps}. \tag{6.18}$$

f_b cannot exceed the lateral flexural strength of the individual masonry units because that strength is not improved by vertical prestress, and so unless this property of the units is known f_{kb} is best limited to 0.9 f_{kx}. Although Eq. 6.18 was developed for clay brick masonry it can be reliably used for concrete blockwork.

If f_{kb} is inserted in Eq. 6.17 and the partial safety factors for material strength and for load are taken as 1.0 the design value for B is

$$B = \{(f_{kb}t_f^2)/(0.6w)\}^{0.5}. \tag{6.19}$$

Near the capping beam and the foundation the loaded leaf will have a bending capacity in the vertical as well as the horizontal direction providing it is not cracked in flexure by moments in the vertical direction. Advantage may be taken of this by designing for the average load on a 1 m height of panel at the top and bottom of the wall.

Slender Walls

When a tall wall is prestressed the prestress must be limited to take account of the slenderness, and possible buckling failure, of the wall.

The strength of a slender wall subjected to vertical load (which includes the prestress force) can be assessed in principle by the methods used for solid walls except that, if the wall's cross-section is of the geometric type, the capacity reduction factor which allows for the effects of the wall's slenderness and the eccentricity of the applied load needs modifying.

The required modifications have been carried out by Phipps for a number of different section shapes.[6.26] As an example, Table 6.2 gives the capacity reduction factors for an 'I'-section which can be used for prestressed diaphragm walls. The factors in Table 6.2 have been conservatively chosen for an 'I'-section which gains minimum benefit from its improved section properties over a solid section of the same thickness so they may be used safely for all diaphragm wall sections.

Table 6.2 Capacity reduction factors due to axial compressive load for an 'I'-section

Slenderness ratio, h/D	Eccentricity at top of 'I'-section wall, e_x					
	Up to 0.05D	0.1D	0.2D	0.3D	0.4D	0.5D
0	1.00	0.90	0.74	0.60	0.38	0
6	1.00	0.90	0.74	0.60	0.38	0
8	1.00	0.90	0.74	0.60	0.38	0
10	0.98	0.90	0.74	0.60	0.38	0
12	0.95	0.89	0.74	0.60	0.38	0
14	0.91	0.85	0.74	0.60	0.38	0
16	0.86	0.81	0.72	0.60	0.38	0
18	0.80	0.75	0.68	0.60	0.38	0
20	0.75	0.72	0.63	0.55	0.38	0
22	0.71	0.67	0.59	0.49	0.28	0
24	0.66	0.62	0.53	0.36	0.13	0
26	0.60	0.56	0.43	0.21	0	0
27	0.57	0.52	0.34	0.11	0	0
28	0.53	0.47	0.26	0.03	0	0
30	0.42	0.30	0.07	0	0	0

Loss of Prestress

As discussed in Chapter 4, in all prestressed structures which use stressed tendons, there is a long-term reduction of prestress with time which has to be allowed for in design. Such losses in walls stem from the same causes as in beams but there will be some differences arising from the form of construction. Thus it will not generally be feasible to stress the tendons in a length of wall simultaneously and to eliminate loss due to elastic shortening of the masonry it will be necessary to restress individual tendons to give a uniform level of stress along the wall. Prestress loss can in any case be reduced in post-tensioned systems by topping up the tendon stress at a relatively early stage after construction. This operation is best performed using at least a pair of jacks working from the ends towards the middle, or vice versa. Uniform prestress can usually be attained after three or four cycles of stress.

Direct Laboratory Measurements of Prestress Losses

It is a relatively simple matter to calculate prestress losses in the manner described in Chapter 4, but the results from such calculations need to be tempered with some judgement. This is because many of the material properties used in the calculations are not often known very accurately and it is not fully understood how the different kinds of loss interact with one another in a real wall.

A number of prestressed walls which have been tested in laboratories to ascertain their strengths are described on pages 139 and 140. In most of these tests losses of prestress were also measured, albeit usually over a fairly short period of a few weeks or months. For instance, loss of prestress over 70 weeks has been measured in the laboratory by Phipps on four concrete blockwork walls, records of the first 40 weeks being published in reference 6.27. To start with, the blockwork was several months old, dry, and had previously been prestressed for lateral load tests. The losses are therefore substantially due to blockwork creep alone. In applying the prestress for loss measurements individual bars were topped up until a uniform level of stress was applied over the walls. All four walls behaved in a similar manner. The losses after 70 weeks were 22, 20, 15 and 13 per cent for the initial prestress levels of 1.0, 1.5, 3.0 and 3.5 N mm^{-2} in each wall respectively. The blockwork was built of 10 N mm^{-2} solid dense aggregate blocks in 1:1:6 mortar. The graph of Fig. 6.21 shows the manner in which the measured prestress decayed with time over the 70-week period.

Fig. 6.21
Prestress losses measured in concrete blockwork diaphragm walls

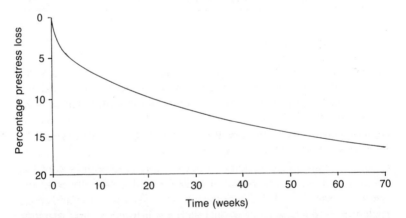

Shrive has summarized short-term measurements on other test walls alongside theoretical long-term predictions of prestress loss.[6.28] He suggests extreme losses of some 30 per cent in concrete blockwork and about 20 per cent in brickwork. The information on losses is still far from complete, however, and such global figures as these should be treated as a guide only.

Losses in the field will be different from laboratory measurements and theoretically computed values but they will decay in a similar way, most loss occurring in the early days. Considerable long-term benefit can be achieved therefore by topping up the prestress at an early age, but whatever practical means are used to reduce losses there is no substitute for an accurate knowledge of the relevant properties of the materials in a wall. If these properties are not known they should be measured to make sure that the behaviour of the wall will be satisfactory in the long term.

Effect of Complete Loss of Prestress

There may be some cases where complete loss of prestress is allowed for. This may be done when prestress is only required in the short term and no special care has been taken to minimize prestress loss, or it may be felt that, because of lack of data on long-term losses in a particular case, it is prudent to check capacity with a zero level of prestress.

So long as the anchorage is not slack, if the whole of the prestress is lost, the wall will behave as a reinforced wall instead of a prestressed one. The performance under the design loads will be different because tension stresses in the masonry will not then be eliminated by compressive prestress. Cracking might therefore occur on the tension side — though it may not necessarily be noticed because it may be on the back of, say, a retaining wall. The behaviour at ultimate will be similar to the prestressed behaviour except that, of course, the effective prestress, f_e, is equal to zero. There are two things to consider: bending strength and shear strength.

For bending, instead of strain compatibility (Eq. 6.8) giving the steel stress an additional equilibrium equation is needed. Referring again to Fig. 6.2(a) and taking moments about the centre of the compression zone,

$$M_u = A_s[f_s/\gamma_{ms}]d[1 - x_1/2].$$ [6.6a]

This equation is used in conjunction with Eq. 6.6 for compression bending strength.

For shear, when the beneficial effects of prestressing are lost, failure in walls is not due to diagonal web cracking but to mortar joint cracking at a lower load. To control this the shear stress, calculated according to Eq. 6.9, is restricted to the normal shear stress levels for unprestressed walls. For tied walls the tie design procedure is the same whether prestress is present or not, providing there is sufficient clamping force to cause the ties to bend.

References

6.1   Ganz H-R 1989 New post-tensioning system for masonry. *Proceedings of the Fifth Canadian Masonry Symposium* Vancouver June 1989 Vol 1 pp 165–75

6.2   Barrett N 1988 Bridge bricks lay future for new civils option. *New Civil Engineer* Feb: 54–5

6.3   Neill J A 1966 *Post-tensioned Brickwork and its Use in the Construction of a Factory at Darlington* Clay Products Technical Bureau Technical Note Vol 1 No 9 4 pp

6.4   Rosenhaupt S, Beresford F D, Blakey F A 1967 Test of a post-tensioned concrete masonry wall. *Proceedings of the American Concrete Institute* **64**: 829−37

6.5   Curtin W G, Phipps M E 1982 Prestressed masonry diaphragm walls. *Proceedings of the Sixth International Brick Masonry Conference* Rome May 1982 pp 971−80

6.6   Curtin W G 1986 An investigation into the structural behaviour of post-tensioned brick diaphragm walls. *The Structural Engineer* **64B**(4) Dec: 77−84

6.7   Curtin W G, Howard J 1988 Lateral loading tests on tall post-tensioned brick diaphragm walls. *Proceedings of the Eighth International Brick/Block Masonry Conference* Dublin Sept 1988 Vol 2 pp 595−605

6.8   Ambrose R J, Hulse R, Mohajery S 1988 Cantilevered prestressed diaphragm walling subjected to lateral loading. *Proceedings of the Eighth International Brick/Block Masonry Conference* Dublin Sept 1988 Vol 2 pp 583−94

6.9   Hobbs B, Daou Y 1988 Post-tensioned T-section brickwork retaining walls. *Proceedings of the Eighth International Brick/Block Masonry Conference* Dublin Sept 1988 Vol 2 pp 665−75

6.10 Garrity S W, Garwood T G 1990 The construction and testing of a full scale prestressed clay brickwork diaphragm wall bridge abutment. *Second International Masonry Conference Proceedings of the British Masonry Society* **4**: London Oct 1989

6.11 Phipps M E, Montague T I 1986 Concrete blockwork diaphragm walls − prestressed and unprestressed. In *Practical Design of Masonry Structures* Thomas Telford, London pp 265−76

6.12 Huizer A, Loov R E 1985 Post-tensioning of single-wythe clay brick masonry walls. *Proceedings of the Seventh International Brick Masonry Conference* Melbourne Feb 1985 pp 993

6.13 Page A W, Huizer A 1988 Racking behaviour of prestressed and reinforced hollow masonry walls. *Masonry International* **2**(3): 97−102

6.14 Williams E O L, Phipps M E 1982 The bending behaviour of prestressed masonry box beams at ultimate. *Proceedings of the Sixth International Brick Masonry Conference* Rome May 1982 pp 981−92

6.15 Phipps M E, Montague T I 1987 The testing of plain and prestressed concrete blockwork beams and walls of geometric cross section. *Masonry International* **1**(3): 71−108

6.16 Roumani N A, Phipps M E 1988 The ultimate shear strength of unbonded prestressed brickwork I and T section members. *Proceedings of the British Masonry Society* Masonry 2, April 1988

6.17 Lokkas P G 1985 The bending strength of masonry sections of unusual shape. MSc thesis, University of Manchester Faculty of Technology

6.18 Phipps M E, Montague T I 1987 *The Design of Prestressed Concrete Blockwork Diaphragm Walls* Aggregate Concrete Block Association, Leicester, England

6.19   Curtin W G, Shaw G, Beck J K, Howard J 1989 *Design of Post-tensioned Brickwork* Brick Development Association, Windsor, England

6.20   British Ceramic Research Association 1977 *Design Guide for Reinforced and Prestressed Clay Brickwork* Special Publication 91

6.21   British Standards Institution 1985 *BS 5628: Code of Practice for Use of Masonry, Part 2: Structural Use of Reinforced and Prestressed Masonry* London

6.22   Ganz H-R 1989 Failure criteria for masonry. *Proceedings of the Fifth Canadian Masonry Symposium* Vancouver June 1989 Vol 1 pp 65–77

6.23   Page A W, Samarasinghe W, Hendry A W 1980 The failure of masonry shear walls. *The International Journal of Masonry Construction* 1(2): 52–7

6.24   Garrity S W, Phipps M E 1988 An experimental study of the influence of vertical prestress on the horizontal flexural strength of clay brickwork. *Proceedings of the Eighth International Brick/Block Masonry Conference* Dublin Sept 1988 Vol 2 pp 642–52

6.25   Baker L R, Padhye P Y, Schulze P N 1980 Torsional resistance from friction between overlapping masonry units. *The International Journal of Masonry Construction* 1(2): 62–6

6.26   Phipps M E 1987 The design of slender masonry walls and columns of geometric cross-section to carry vertical load. *The Structural Engineer* **65A**(12): 443–7

6.27   Phipps M E 1986 Discussion on paper 19. In *Practical Design of Masonry Structures* Thomas Telford, London pp 277–84

6.28   Shrive N G 1988 Effects of time dependent movements in composite and post-tensioned masonry. *Masonry International* **2**(1): 25–9

7   Reinforced Masonry Shear Walls and Buildings under Static Load

Professor J C Scrivener, University of Melbourne

Introduction

A shear wall carries in-plane horizontal loads, generated by wind or earthquake, and distributed to the wall primarily via diaphragms such as floors or roof.

This chapter deals only with the effect of static loads on shear walls. The behaviour under seismic or other dynamic loading is the subject of Chapter 8.

Failure of Shear Walls

The name 'shear wall' is not particularly helpful as the behaviour of a wall and its failure mode may be in a mode other than shear. Shear walls subject to horizontal loads, often termed 'racking loads', may fail in one of three ways: by sliding horizontally, in flexure, or in shear. These types of failure are shown diagrammatically in Fig. 7.1.

Sliding Failure

Sliding failure, which is the movement of entire parts of the wall on the base or other mortar bed, is resisted by dowel action of the vertical reinforcement or of the starter bars anchored in the base and by friction on the mortar bed. Usually it is not a problem for a reinforced masonry shear wall within a bulding, though with high horizontal loads it needs to be checked. However, when the shear wall is bedded on a vapour barrier or damp-proof course, the friction resistance may be negligible and this may create a problem particularly in unreinforced walls.

Flexural Failure

In the flexural situation, where the wall behaves as a vertical cantilever or beam, either yielding of the tensile reinforcement near the wall heel or crushing of the masonry at the wall toe may limit the carrying capacity.

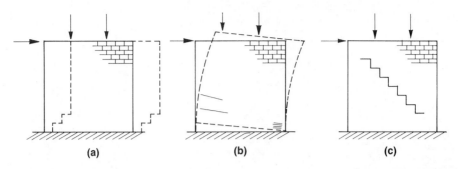

Fig. 7.1 Reinforced
masonry shear
wall failure modes:
(a) sliding failure;
(b) flexural failure;
(c) shear failure

Researchers have been able to predict the strength of a wall for the case of yielding of tensile reinforcement. Scrivener[7.1] found that the maximum horizontal load could be found by equating the moment of the load about the wall base to the sum of the moments of the vertical reinforcement yield forces taken about the wall toe. With light reinforcement concentrated at the wall ends, little error is made in assuming the wall toe to be the location of the resultant flexural compressive force. In a test series with bearing loads and static cyclic in-plane horizontal loading, Scrivener and Williams[7.2] extended the approach to incorporate the moment effect of the bearing load and achieved good predictions of failure load. In some tests, however, Williams[7.3] found that the agreement between test and theory was better when the ultimate strength of the reinforcement was taken rather than the yield strength. Meli[7.4] satisfactorily predicted results in the same manner using yield strengths and assuming that the compressive force acted at the centre of the extreme reinforcement. Later, using reinforced concrete ultimate strengths and strains, Priestley and Bridgeman[7.5] satisfactorily predicted experimental maximum loads.

For the case of failure due to toe crushing, the level of compression stress due to the bearing load and its eccentricity (if any), together with the moment effect of the horizontal racking load can be easily calculated. Page[7.6] has shown that, for solid masonry units, the uniaxial compressive strength will conservatively underestimate the failure load for most situations. With the higher racking loads possible in the reinforced situation, the stress level at the toe may need to be calculated. Should failure occur there it will be in a splitting mode, as obtained in compressively loaded masonry prisms, perhaps with some spalling of the faces of the masonry units.

Shear Failure

Before consideration of walls failing in shear it is necessary to consider the behaviour of masonry in shear and compression.

Fig. 7.2 Angled
compressive
loading of masonry
element

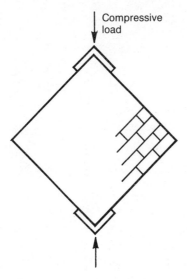

Compressive
load

Masonry in Shear and Compression

There have been many tests[7.6–7.11] on masonry elemental walls, very often using diagonal compressive loading as shown in Fig. 7.2, to provide combined compression and shear on the mortar beds.

As the boundary conditions, load application and masonry material characteristics varied greatly in these tests, the results from the various investigations have been difficult to compare. Accordingly, the strength of masonry subjected to combined compression and shear is usually expressed in terms of the average shear stress and average normal stress obtained by dividing the horizontal racking force and vertical forces respectively by the bed joint area.

The Coulomb form is most often used:

$$v = v_0 + \mu f_n \qquad [7.1]$$

where v = shear strength at compressive stress f_n;

v_0 = shear strength at zero compression;

μ = apparent friction coefficient.

Hendry[7.12] in analysing the results of various investigations, showed that v_0 varied between 0.14 and 0.70 N mm^{-2} and that μ varied between 0.20 and 1.04.

The shear strength of a masonry wall is then:

$$V = A_b v \qquad [7.2]$$

where A_b is the effective cross-sectional area of wall.

Shear strength at zero compression v_0 is sometimes taken as a larger value when considering shear perpendicular to bed joints than the value when considering shear parallel to the bed joints. The effective cross-sectional area is the mortar bedded area which for solid units is usually the entire cross-section but for the hollow units may only be the area of the faces of the units. Should the hollow units be grout filled then A_b should also include the grout area.

The effect of the reinforcement on the shear strength will be considered in the section on wall tests.

Reinforced Walls Failing in Shear

In the 1940s on the West Coast of the USA and in the 1950s in New Zealand, reinforced masonry became a popular and relatively inexpensive means to resist seismic loads and to provide some ductility to normally brittle masonry. The availability of hollow concrete blocks was a significant factor in this phenomenon. While structural designers were using the 'new' material, designed as if it were reinforced concrete, the statutory authorities became concerned that the load, stress and strain limitations of the material were unknown. And so began a number of test programmes in the two countries, in particular, to determine behaviour and to quantify shear strengths and later ductilities.

To ensure that the test wall failed in shear rather than in flexure, the researchers needed to:

(a) have no bending moments on the wall, or
(b) counteract the bending moment, or
(c) create a situation where the bending moment capacity exceeded the shear capacity so that the test wall failed in shear.

The objective was achieved in a variety of means as illustrated in Fig. 7.3.

It is obvious that each researcher sought a method of testing which predicted, as closely as possible, the real situation in a structure, while maintaining an acceptable test method.

There are objections to each method. For instance, the large compressive force in the external holding-down situation of Fig. 7.3(a) may have a considerable effect on the shear stresses and strains in the wall locally, and generally as it adds concentrated bearing load. The internal holding-down method of Fig. 7.3(b) does overcome the above problem but in the attempt to ensure a shear failure it may be necessary to incorporate large amounts of peripheral vertical reinforcement. These amounts of reinforcement may not reflect the real situation. Methods (c) and (d) of Fig. 7.3 do not represent the true loading situation in a structure. The need for struts in the openings of method 3(d) creates an artificial structure but the effect may be negligible on the central pier which is the essential structure being tested.

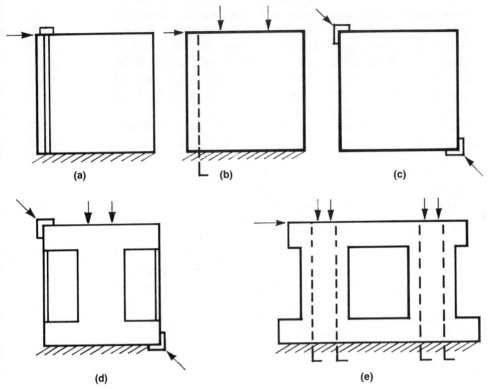

Fig. 7.3 Methods of testing shear walls: (a) external hold-down; (b) internal hold-down; (c) diagonal compression; (d) diagonal compression on piers; (e) fixed-ended piers

In a recent test series in the USA using cyclic loadings, Mayes and Clough[7.13] used the method of Fig. 7.3(e) to approximate the boundary conditions of piers in a complete structure. Researchers in New Zealand and elsewhere have tended to remain with the internal hold-down method of Fig. 7.3(b) as representing a realistic situation, particularly where there is a top beam able to distribute the racking load appropriately and a heavy base beam so that the method of securement to the test floor does not influence the wall behaviour.

In 1946 Converse[7.14] reported to the (US) Pacific Coast building officials on shear tests of nine walls constructed in reinforced hollow concrete masonry units. His loading method was essentially that of Fig. 7.3(c) so his failures were in diagonal cracks. He noted that the failure load increased with additional reinforcement whether it was horizontal or vertical.

Three series of tests were conducted by Schneider. The first series,[7.15] in 1956, used cavity clay brickwork tested in method (a) of Fig. 7.3, and he had some walls failing in flexure and some in shear. He observed that the flexural stresses in relatively high walls needed to be recognized by placing adequate vertical reinforcement at the pier boundaries. Further, the allowable (design) shear value should be dependent on the height/depth ratio of the wall whereas at the time of reporting it had a single value in California.

In his second series of tests,[7.16] using method (b) of Fig. 7.3, Schneider confirmed his earlier findings. He also found that a 50 per cent increase in the reinforcement percentage in his concrete block walls did not have an appreciable effect upon the ultimate capacity but did increase the load to produce the initial cracks in the walls.

New Zealand research on reinforced masonry shear walls was commenced by Scrivener[7.1] in 1966 as reported earlier within the flexural failure section. At the first international masonry conference in Austin, Texas in 1967, he reported[7.17] test results on concrete masonry walls failing in shear using the external holding-down method of Fig. 7.3(a). Scrivener's findings were:

1. Vertical and horizontal reinforcement appeared to be equally effective in providing satisfactory crack behaviour and failure loads.
2. Walls with evenly distributed reinforcement have a later onset of severe cracking (where crack widths exceed 0.25 mm) than walls with reinforcement only on the periphery.
3. The load gap between severe cracking and failure is greater in walls with higher reinforcement percentages.
4. The shear strength increased to 1.17 N mm^{-2} with increasing reinforcement up to an optimum of 0.3 per cent.

Schneider's third series of tests[7.18] was extensive, involving cantilever piers and 'fixed-end' piers, the latter obtained by constructing a heavy spandrel beam above the pier in addition to the heavy base beam of the cantilever piers. Also the height/width dimensions of the piers were varied. His method of test was that of Fig. 7.3(d). A major finding reported was that the average shear strength increased with a decrease in the height/width ratio of the pier, with a rapid rate of increase of strength when the ratio was between 3:1 and 1:1. Heavy amounts of horizontal reinforcement enhanced the behaviour of the pier and increased the capacity whereas the shear resistance was not significantly increased with increase in the peripheral (or jamb) reinforcement. Shear strength and pier stiffness also increased with the bearing load increase.

The research of Meli[7.4] in Mexico in 1972 gave similar findings to those reported above. His test series included comparisons of identical walls some with bearing loads and some without. The shear strength increased with the increase in bearing load and tended to change the failure mode from flexure to shear.

In 1981 the draft British code[7.19] gave the characteristic shear strength for brickwork shear walls (v_k) as

$$v_k = 0.35 + 0.6f_n \text{ N mm}^{-2} \qquad\qquad [7.3]$$

with a maximum of 1.75 N mm^{-2}.

This was the same strength as that for unreinforced walls. Accordingly a shear test series on reinforced clay brickwork walls was conducted at the University of Edinburgh. Scrivener[7.20] reported that the walls were tested by the method (b) of Fig. 7.3 and most walls failed in shear. The shear resistance at first crack was remarkably consistent at an average of 0.69 N mm^{-2}. The walls had height/width ratios of 0.78−1.7 with percentages of vertical reinforcement varying from 0.19 to 0.76 per cent. Each wall had 6−8 mm diameter bars as horizontal reinforcement. By and large, the shear resistance increased with reduction in height/width ratio and with increased percentage of vertical reinforcement. The ultimate shear strength ranged between 0.72 and 1.15 N mm^{-2}, suggesting that the 0.35 N mm^{-2} code proposal figure was unduly conservative for common aspect ratios and percentages of reinforcement.

Further tests on reinforced masonry shear walls concentrating on aseismic performance have been conducted by Meli,[7.4] Mayes and Clough,[7.13] Priestley and Bridgeman,[7.5] Scrivener and Williams[7.2] and Williams.[7.3]

A finding of Priestley and Bridgeman[7.5] is most relevant to the static behaviour of reinforced masonry shear walls. They showed, theoretically and experimentally, the incorrect perception of earlier researchers who considered that vertical and horizontal reinforcement were equally effective in resisting shear. Their argument is that prior to cracking, the principal tensile stresses near the middle of a panel are 45° approximately to the vertical, resulting in the formation of the diagonal crack. After the crack is formed, the racking load tends to move the top part of the wall horizontally as shown in Fig. 7.4. Now the resistance of the horizontal reinforcement is in direct tension, whereas the vertical reinforcement carries the racking load by dowel action. Their calculations indicate that accordingly the horizontal reinforcement is more than three times as effective as the vertical reinforcement.

Priestley and Bridgeman further point out that in the earlier work of Schneider[7.16] and Scrivener,[7.12] using percentages of reinforcement below 0.3 per cent, insufficient shear steel was provided to carry the full shear load, which explains their findings that vertical and horizontal reinforcement were equally effective. Priestley and Bridgeman and others have since developed the theory and practice of using higher percentages of horizontal reinforcement with great effect.

It is interesting to note that the shear wall tests of the various researchers confirmed some simple theoretical points. Consider the shear wall of Fig. 7.5. Taking moments about the wall toe at B, and assuming this point to be the centroid of the compression block (as per Scrivener[7.1]),

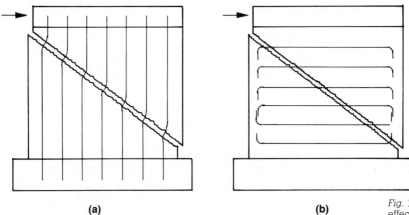

(a)   (b)

Fig. 7.4 Relative
effectiveness of
vertical and
horizontal shear
reinforcement
(from Priestley and
Bridgeman[7.5]): (a)
vertical shear
reinforcement in
dowel action; (b)
horizontal shear
reinforcement in
tension

for equilibrium at yield of the tensile reinforcement,

$$Vh \approx f_y A_s l + Nl/2.$$ [7.4]

Equation 7.4 indicates that to increase the flexural capacity of the wall
to the racking load (V) one can:

(a) reduce the height (h)/length (l) ratio of the wall;
(b) increase the reinforcement yield strength (f_y) and the area of the
     tensile reinforcement (A_s);
(c) increase the bearing load.

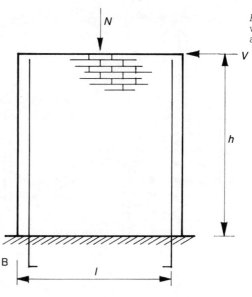

Fig. 7.5 Shear
wall under vertical
and racking loads

However, the tests of the researchers quantified these effects for various geometries and materials.

This simple model also shows that as a designer follows the trends of (a), (b) and (c) above to increase the wall flexural capacity, the wall may be forced to fail in shear creating a situation which may not be the most desirable.

Shear Walls in Buildings

Consider a building in which the lateral load resistance is primarily provided by shear walls. The horizontal wind loads act on an end, or transverse, wall of the building which transmits the loads to the adjacent floors or roof, above and below it. These floors act as horizontal beams, termed diaphragms, spanning between the longitudinal walls. Horizontal forces are transmitted to the longitudinal walls as in-plane forces and hence these walls are shear walls. The shear walls also carry vertical bearing forces transmitted by the floors or roof. Figure 7.6 gives a pictorial view of these actions.

The fraction of the horizontal wind load which each shear wall of a building will carry depends on two factors:

(a) the stiffness of the diaphragms;
(b) the arrangement and relative stiffnesses of the shear walls.

Fig. 7.6
Transmission of wind loads to shear walls

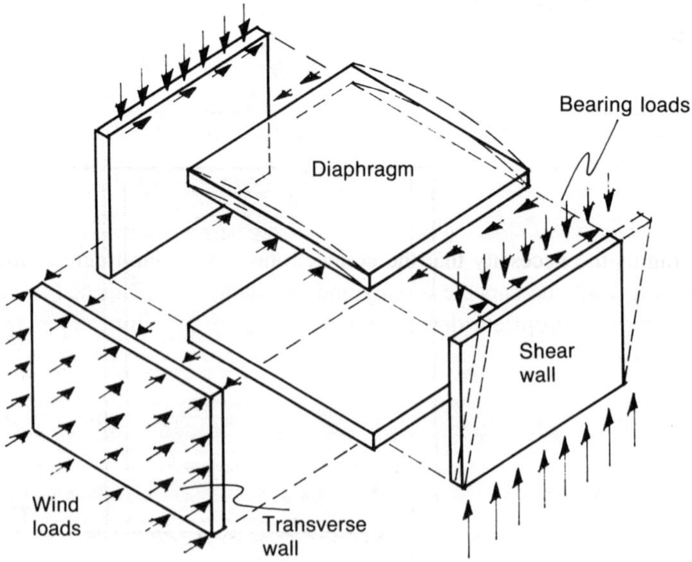

Diaphragms

For satisfactory performance a diaphragm must be able to transmit the horizontal forces so that the in-plane deflection is not so large that it is deleterious to the transverse wall.

Diaphragms are classified as rigid or flexible. A rigid diaphragm is one in which the in-plane deflections are so small that it is reasonable to assume that the horizontal forces are distributed to the shear walls in proportion to their relative stiffnesses. Rigid diaphragms are also capable of transmitting rotational forces created when the shear centre of the shear wall system does not lie on the line of action of the resultant horizontal wind force, as discussed in the later section on systems of shear walls.

With flexible diaphragms, the horizontal forces produce significant deflections so that the distribution of forces between the shear walls will depend not only on the arrangement and relative stiffnesses of the shear walls but also on the stiffness of the diaphragm. Where the diaphragm is of irregular plan, say 'T', 'L' or 'Z' shaped, the disparity of deflections at the boundaries between different sized and shaped sub-areas can create tearing forces. If these forces are large enough, an additional strengthening to transmit shear forces from the diaphragm to the shear walls may be required. Amrhein[7.21] shows that the distribution of the force to the shear walls is in proportion to the tributary areas of the diaphragm adjacent to the shear walls and strengthening and he gives a numerical example of the calculations required.

Codes generally specify maximum span to width or depth ratios of diaphragms to control diaphragm deflections.

Diaphragms may be constructed of any construction material. When a diaphragm is made up from discrete units such as plywood, precast concrete planks or steel decking, the method of attachment of the units to each other is crucial in obtaining sufficient in-plane stiffness. *In situ* reinforced concrete may not have this problem but it shares with all diaphragms the necessity that the connections of the diaphragm to the supporting walls be capable of carrying the shear forces needed to be transmitted. Appropriate design and detailing of the connections are essential.

Shear Wall Stiffness

Rigid diaphragms ensure that shear walls connected by diaphragms deflect equally under horizontal load and the proportion of this load carried by each shear wall is determined by its relative stiffness. The stiffness of

Fig. 7.7 Moment
and shear
deflections of
shear wall: (a)
cantilevered wall;
(b) fixed-ended
wall

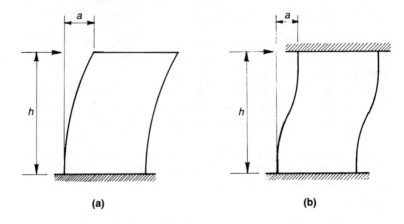

(a)   (b)

a shear wall is inversely proportional to its deflection under unit horizontal
load.

The deflection of a shear wall is the sum of the deflections due to shear
and moment. The moment deflection depends on whether the wall is
cantilevered from its base or fixed at both the top and bottom of the wall.
Figure 7.7 illustrates these two cases to which the following equations
apply. For a wall fixed at both top and bottom, the moment deflection
(a_m) is

$$a_m = \frac{Vh^3}{12\,E_m I}.$$ [7.5]

For a wall cantilevered from the base, the moment deflection (a_m) is

$$a_m = \frac{Vh^3}{3\,E_m I}$$ [7.6]

For a fixed or cantilevered wall, the shear deflection (a_v) is

$$a_v = \frac{\alpha_s\,Vh}{G_m\,A}$$ [7.7]

where V = racking load;
       h = wall height;
       A = wall cross-sectional area;
       I = second moment of area of wall about the relevant
           axis;
      E_m = modulus of elasticity of the masonry;
      G_m = modulus of rigidity of the masonry;
           = $0.4E_m$;
      α_s = shear deformation coefficient (1.2 for a rectangular
           section, 1.0 for a flanged section).

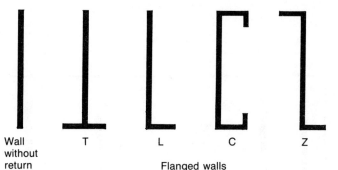

Fig. 7.8 Shear wall returns

Wall without return   T   L   C   Z

Flanged walls

The total deflection (*a*) is

$$a = a_m + a_v \qquad\qquad [7.8]$$

and the wall stiffness is inversely proportional to the total deflection.

It can be shown that for multi-storey buildings of usual proportions, the moment deflection at the top of the building greatly exceeds the shear deflection so that only the flexural stiffness need be considered in determining the relative stiffness of such a shear wall. For uniform wind load, SCPI[7.22] shows that where a building is five times higher than its length the moment deflection is 90 per cent of the total deflection. For buildings higher than this the shear deflection becomes even more negligible relative to the moment deflection.

Much enhanced second moments of area (moments of inertia) can be obtained when a shear wall has a flange or flanges as shown in Fig. 7.8. The increase in moment of inertia leads to an increased stiffness and to reductions in maximum bending and shear stresses. The flange may be formed by a return at the end of the shear wall or by incorporation of part of an intersecting wall. Codes have adopted simple rules for the effective widths of such returns for the cases of 'T', 'L', 'C' and 'Z'-sections. With these effective widths, the calculation for the enhanced moment of inertia, using traditional engineering mechanics principles, may be conducted.

Before accepting the enhanced moments of inertia, designers need to be certain that the capacity of the connection of the main wall and the return is sufficient to transmit the shear stresses existing. The effect of openings above or below the intersection must be considered.

Systems of Shear Walls

Where the arrangement of a system of shear walls is entirely symmetrical and the line of action of the resultant wind load is along the line of

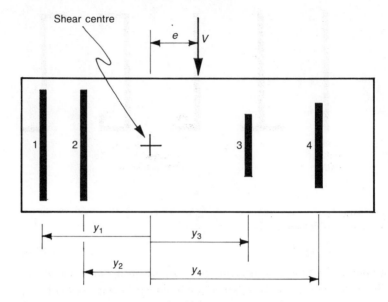

Fig. 7.9 Shear walls in a symmetrical arrangement

symmetry, the distribution of wind forces to the various shear walls is straightforward.

In the asymmetrical situation, the shear centre is unlikely to lie on the line of action of the load. Hence a twisting moment, about a vertical axis, has to be resisted by the diaphragm and the individual walls will receive further shear loads to equilibrate this twisting moment. These additional shears may or may not be in the same direction as the 'direct' shear due to the wind load. Figure 7.9 illustrates such a situation.

The load resisted by an individual shear wall (V_n) will then be, as proved by Hendry, Sinha and Davies,[7.23] the summation of the effect of the total load (V) as if it were applied at the shear centre together with the moment effect of V about the shear centre.

$$V_n = \frac{VI_n}{\Sigma I} + \frac{Vey_nI_n}{\Sigma Iy^2}$$

[7.9]

where I_n = moment of inertia of wall;
y_n = distance of wall from the shear centre;
e = eccentricity of shear centre from centre line.

As y_n may be positive or negative so the second term may be either additive or subtractive to the first term. It is additive for walls on the same side of the shear centre as is the load V.

From the second term of Eq. 7.9, it is apparent that most resistance to the twisting moment is given by walls at large distances from the shear centre. It is good engineering practice to provide as large a 'lever arm' as possible for shear walls, even in the case of symmetrically positioned shear walls, as there is always the possibility of twisting moments occurring due to circumstances unknown to the designer. Some codes insist upon the structure being capable of carrying an arbitrary torsional moment calculated from the storey shear and an eccentricity related to the appropriate maximum plan dimension. Under these circumstances, a rigid diaphragm is essential to carry the torsional moment and its resulting shears to the shear walls.

Shear Walls with Openings

Openings such as doors and windows reduce the stiffness of a shear wall from that of an unpierced wall. To calculate the reduced stiffness and to determine the proportions of the shear force carried by each part of a wall, it is necessary to calculate the relative stiffnesses of the various parts. For a single-storey wall with windows and doors, Amrhein[7.21] calculates in considerable detail the stiffness of the parts of a wall and determines the reinforcement necessary in each part to carry the shear forces.

The very presence of openings in a wall can precipitate cracks originating from the corners of the openings. Accordingly reinforcement additional to that calculated above should be provided both horizontally and vertically near each corner of an opening.

The placement of openings can greatly vary the overall stiffness of a wall. Amrhein[7.21] considers an eight-storey shear wall with two storey-height openings at each level and compares the relative stiffnesses of walls with different opening patterns. He assumes that the floors connecting the wall portions are flexible and do not transfer shear or moment. Taking a wall with no openings to have a stiffness of 100 units, he gives an example of a wall with scattered openings which has a stiffness of 70 units. Shear walls with openings stacked on top of each other act as a series of units, with the larger stiffness occurring when the stack of openings allows of a relatively long length of unpierced wall element.

Coupled Shear Walls

When a relatively stiff member connects wall elements, a coupled shear wall system is created. In an example of an eight-storey shear wall with one set of openings, Amrhein[7.21] compares the relative stiffness of an unpierced wall of stiffness 100 units with coupled shear walls, one with a large coupling beam so that the wall stiffness is 92 units and the other with a smaller coupling beam which results in a wall stiffness of 50 units. The equivalent 'uncoupled' wall system has a stiffness of 18 units.

Hendry[7.12] gives five basic methods of analysis of coupled shear walls and these are illustrated in Fig. 7.10(b)−(f).

Fig. 7.10 Basic
methods of
analysis of
coupled shear
walls (from
Hendry[7.12]): (a)
shear wall with
openings; (b)
cantilever method;
(c) shear
continuum; (d)
frame analogy; (e)
wide column
frame analogy; (f)
finite element

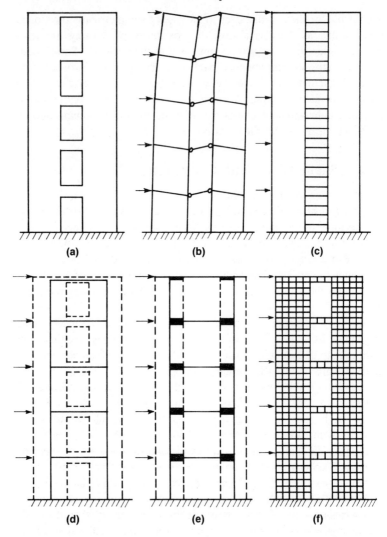

In the cantilever method Fig. 7.10(b), the structure is assumed to be
a series of vertical cantilever walls which deflect together as the coupling
does not transmit moments and shears but only direct forces. So the
coupling is represented by pin-ended links. The wind forces are
distributed to the walls in proportion to their relative stiffnesses. This
is the conventional design method for unreinforced masonry shear walls
and for many reinforced masonry shear walls where the coupling is a
flexible floor slab only.

In the equivalent frame method Fig. 7.10(c), the walls and slabs are
replaced by columns and beams of the same stiffnesses, and the beams

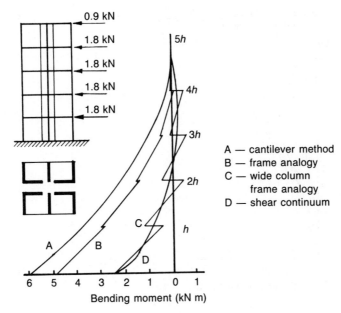

Fig. 7.11 Bending moments from test and analyses of coupled shear wall (from Hendry[7.12])

A — cantilever method
B — frame analogy
C — wide column
      frame analogy
D — shear continuum

span between the centroidal axes of the columns. The wall is now analysed as a rigid frame.

The wide column frame method, Fig. 7.10(d), is a refinement on the equivalent frame method with the coupling members assumed to be of infinite stiffness for the part of their length from the centroidal axis of the column to the opening.

Where the couplings are replaced by an equivalent shear medium continuous over the height of the walls, the shear continuum method, Fig. 7.10(e), is obtained. A point of contraflexure may be assumed at the centre of the shear medium.

Finite element analysis, Fig. 7.10(f), is the fifth method in which the structure is divided into a number of triangular or rectangular elements which are connected only at their nodes. Equilibrium and compatibility conditions lead to a number of simultaneous equations which can be computer solved.

Hendry[7.12] compares these analyses for a particular five-storey unreinforced clay brickwork building which was built and tested at Edinburgh University. Comparisons of bending moments are given in Fig. 7.11 and of deflections in Fig. 7.12. These two figures show that the cantilever method overestimates both the bending moments and the deflections. Accordingly the cantilever method, which is the simplest to calculate, is suggested by Hendry to be a useful preliminary design tool to determine whether the wind loading is likely to be crucial in a

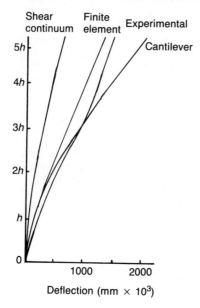

Fig. 7.12
Deflections from
test and analyses
of coupled shear
wall (from
Hendry[7.12])

given case. He did, however, issue the warning that while the cantilever
method assumes no bending in the coupling, bending does occur there
and it needs to be designed for.

The best approximation to the actual behaviour was given by the
equivalent frame method. The wide column frame and the continuum
methods were less satisfactory. The finite element method may be
justified but only in special cases due to its complexity as a design tool.

The behaviour and design of reinforced *concrete* shear walls has
received considerable attention by researchers and designers. Irwin[7.24]
considers the elastic design of shear and core walls, discussing pierced
walls, analysis of flanged walls and their effective heights, structural
interaction of walls and frames, three-dimensional analysis and computer
modelling and he includes some design charts. His report then considers
dynamic and seismic analyses. It is extensively referenced.

While the principles of behaviour of coupled shear walls will not differ
markedly from unreinforced to reinforced masonry, the designer of
reinforced masonry shear walls will need to borrow information and
expertise from reinforced concrete researchers and designers. With the
ability of reinforced masonry to carry higher shear forces than
unreinforced masonry, the designer may wish to increase the building
stiffness by using more substantial coupling beams. Then the design of
the coupling beam becomes a crucial part of the design, and the behaviour
and design of reinforced concrete coupling beams should be studied.

Masonry Infill Panels

Where a frame of reinforced concrete or steel has masonry built right up to the inside of beams and columns, a masonry infill panel results.

The behaviour of an infill panel under increasing horizontal racking load follows three major phases according to Leuchars and Scrivener.[7.25]

Initial Phase

During this phase, the infill and the frame are in intimate contact and they deform together. Horizontal deformations are the summation of moment and shear effects and may be calculated by standard elastic structural theory. The system is much stiffer than the frame alone and also resists a greater racking load before significant cracking occurs. For example, in the tests of Leuchars and Scrivener[7.25] of a clay brick infill within a reinforced concrete frame, the infill panel was 30 times stiffer and had 6 times more load capacity to significant cracking than the frame alone.

The duration of the phase depends largely on the bond between the infill and the frame. Shear connectors between the infill and frame have been shown by Mallick and Garg[7.26] to increase the duration of the uncracked phase but premature cracking of the infill can occur.

With a reinforced concrete frame, the phase may continue up to 50 per cent of the ultimate load of the system and so may encompass the normal service load situation.

When flexure predominates the system acts as a vertical cantilever and horizontal cracks may open on the tension side of the frame and infill. Alternatively where shear is more dominant cracks on the diagonally opposite tension interfaces may occur. The phase ends when the differences in deflection behaviour of the frame and infill become too great and vertical cracks develop along the interfaces.

Phase after Interface Cracking

The separation between the frame and infill occurs along the interfaces except near the ends of the compression diagonal as shown in Fig. 7.13. The infill is now acting much as a diagonal strut within the frame. Analogous frames have been proposed by Holmes[7.27] and by Smith and Carter[7.28] who suggested that the strut width depends on the length of contact between the frame and the infill (itself depending on the relative stiffness of columns and infill, the length/height of the infill and the stress−strain relationship of the infill material). As both stiffnesses alter

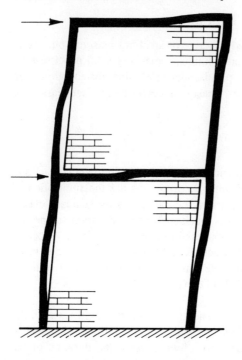

Fig. 7.13
Separation of
frame and infill in
masonry infill
panel under
horizontal loads

with the extent of cracking, the equivalent strut width alters throughout loading. Several researchers have found, however, that the Smith and Carter theory does predict the stiffness reasonably though it is not a good predictor of ultimate load.

Failure Phase

Provided that the frame has sufficient strength, the masonry infill panel may fail in one or a combination of the following modes:

(a) sliding failure along a horizontal mortar bed;
(b) diagonal cracking;
(c) local crushing at the ends of the compression diagonal.

The tests of Esteva,[7.29] on square infill within reinforced concrete frames, indicate that the failure mechanism of the infill was little influenced by the frame characteristics. Diagonal cracking of the panel occurred regardless of the frame cross-section, corner reinforcement or frame diagonal strength.

On the other hand, the manner of the infill failure greatly influences the failure of the frame as it determines the way in which the frame is loaded. Fiarato, Sozen and Gamble[7.30] tested systems where the infill lengths were twice the heights. With many tests the infill cracks were

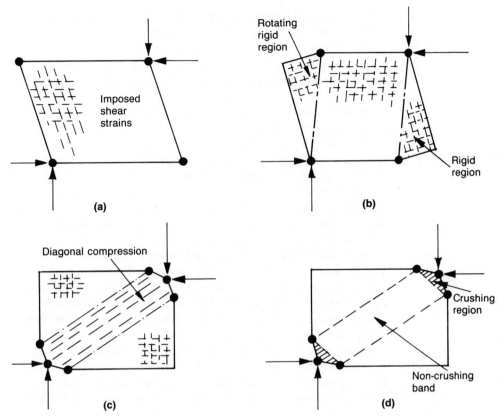

(a)

Imposed shear strains

(b)

Rotating rigid region

Rigid region

(c)

Diagonal compression

(d)

Crushing region

Non-crushing band

Fig. 7.14 Idealized plastic failure modes for masonry infill panels (from Wood[7.31])

horizontal along mortar beds and these cracks precipitated failure in the frame columns either in flexure, with plastic hinges developing at the crack level and at the column top or base, or in shear at the crack level.

Wood[7.31] reports that full-scale tests, at the (UK) Building Research Establishment from 1953 to 1970, produced several different types of collapse which were not predicted theoretically. He identified a trend in the collapse modes which is illustrated in Fig. 7.14.

The shear mode of Fig. 7.14(a) is the case where the frame is very strong and the infill weak so that the beams and columns remain straight and the wall distorts in a pure shear manner. Plastic hinges form at the joints of the frame.

With a relatively stronger infill, a plastic hinge appears in each beam, suggesting compressive action in the infill. In tests failing in this mode, the shear rotation mode of Fig. 7.14(b), the unloaded corners merely underwent a rigid body rotation. Where the beams of the frame are relatively strong, the column may be forced to yield leading to the 'knee-braced' concept named by Fiarato, Sozen and Gamble.[7.30]

Where the wall is strong and the frame relatively weak, the diagonal compression mode of Fig. 7.14(c), the beam plastic hinge of the shear rotation mode appears close to the loaded corners and a similar plastic hinge occurs in the column. The weaker is the beam the more localized is the diagonal compression and it may lead to corner crushing (Fig. 7.14(d)).

Wood[7.31] developed the equations which apply in each of these failure modes and produced extensive and relatively simple rules for design. He introduced a penalty factor to cater for the discrepancy between his theoretical prediction and experimental results which lowers the effective crushing strength of the infill in order to account for imperfect plasticity. He did, however, point out that research is needed into various areas including the effect of openings in walls, the behaviour of reinforced walls with and without connectors, and plastic properties of walls before full design rules can be formulated.

Liauw and Kwan[7.32, 7.33] extended Wood's approach, taking into account stress redistribution during collapse. They believe that the overestimation of the collapse shear of Wood's theory might not be due as much to the lack of plasticity of the infill panels but as a consequence of the excessive friction assumed at the structural interface and the neglect of separation in the composite shear mode.

Where frame and infill are not built integrally, a number of problems may occur, according to Liauw and Kwan.[7.33] The failure is sudden with little warning, the infill can fall out of the frame at failure creating a dangerous situation and the irregularity and unevenness at the interface due to workmanship and infill shrinkage produce considerable variation in the strength and stiffness of the system thus making it unreliable for theoretical prediction and design purposes. With integral infilled frames improved structural behaviour has been demonstrated. Liauw and Kwan and others have provided a deeper understanding of the behaviour of integral infilled frames.

Masonry infill panels with openings are reported in the proceedings of two recent masonry international conferences.[7.34, 7.35]

It is somewhat surprising that little research appears to have been conducted on reinforced masonry infills.

References

7.1   Scrivener J C 1966 Concrete masonry wall panel tests — static racking tests with predominant flexural effect. *New Zealand Concrete Construction* July

7.2   Scrivener J C, Williams D 1971 Behaviour of reinforced masonry shear walls under cyclic loading. *Bulletin of the New Zealand Society for Earthquake Engineering* **4**(2)

7.3   Williams D 1971 Seismic behaviour of reinforced masonry shear walls. PhD thesis, University of Canterbury, New Zealand

7.4   Meli R 1972 Behaviour of masonry walls under lateral loads. In *Proceedings of the Fifth World Conference of Earthquake Engineering* Rome 1972

7.5   Priestley M J N, Bridgeman D O 1974 Seismic resistance of brick masonry walls. *Bulletin of the New Zealand Society for Earthquake Engineering* **7**(4)

7.6   Page A W 1981 The bi-axial compressive strength of brick masonry. *Proceedings of the Institution of Civil Engineers* London, Part 2 **71** Sept: 893–906

7.7   Page A W 1983 The strength of brick masonry under bi-axial tension–compression. *International Journal of Masonry Construction* **3**(1)

7.8   Samarasinghe W, Hendry A W 1982 The strength of brickwork under bi-axial and tensile and compressive stress. *Proceedings of the British Ceramic Society*, Loadbearing Brickwork (7), Sept 1982, **30**: 129–39

7.9   Blume J A 1968 *Shear on Grouted Masonry Wall Elements* Western States Clay Products Association, San Francisco

7.10 Omoto Y, Mayes R L, Clough R W, Chen S W 1977 Effect of test technique on masonry shear strength. *Proceedings of World Conference on Earthquake Engineering* New Delhi Jan 1977 Vol 3 pp 3208–13

7.11 Baba A, Senbu O, Arinaga S 1988 Shear strength of grouted masonry components subjected to diagonal compressive load. In de Courcy J W (ed) *Proceedings of the Eighth International Brick/Block Masonry Conference*, Dublin Sept 1988 Vol 6, pp 491–502

7.12 Hendry A W 1990 *Structural Masonry* Macmillan, London

7.13 Mayes R L, Clough R W 1975 Cyclic shear tests on fixed-ended masonry piers. In *American Society of Civil Engineers, National Structural Engineering Convention* New Orleans April 1975

7.14 Converse F J 1946 Tests on reinforced concrete masonry. *Building Standards Monthly* Feb: 4–13

7.15 Schneider R R 1956 *Investigation of Reinforced Brick Masonry under Lateral Loads* State of California, Division of Architecture, Sacramento

7.16 Schneider R R 1959 *Lateral Load Tests on Reinforced Grouted Masonry Shear Walls* State of California, Division of Architecture, Sacramento

7.17 Scrivener J C 1967 Static racking tests on masonry walls. Proceedings of the International Conference on Masonry Structural Systems, Austin, 1967, published in Johnson F B (ed) *Designing, Engineering and Constructing with Masonry Products* Gulf, Houston pp 185–99

7.18 Schneider R R 1969 *Shear in Concrete Masonry Piers* California State Polytechnic College, Pomona

7.19 British Standards Institution 1981 *Code of Practice for the Structural Use of Masonry Draft Part 2, Reinforced and Prestressed Masonry BS 5628* May 1981

7.20 Scrivener J C 1982 *Shear Tests on Reinforced Brick Masonry Walls* British Ceramic Research Association Technical Note No 342, Oct 1982

7.21 Amrhein J E 1973 *Reinforced Masonry Engineering Handbook — Clay and Concrete Masonry* 2nd edn Masonry Institute of America, Los Angeles and Western States Clay Products Association, San Francisco

7.22   Structural Clay Products Institute 1970 *The Contemporary Bearing Wall — Introduction to Shear Wall Design* Technical Notes on Brick and Tile Construction 24C, Structural Clay Products Institute, McLean, Virginia, Sept–Oct 1970

7.23   Hendry A W, Sinha B P, Davies S R 1981 *An Introduction to Load Bearing Brickwork Design* Ellis Horwood Series in Engineering Science

7.24   Irwin A W 1984 *Design of Shear Wall Buildings* Construction Industry Research and Information Association Report 102, London

7.25   Leuchars J M, Scrivener J C 1976 Masonry infill panels subjected to cyclic in-plane loading. *Bulletin of the New Zealand National Society for Earthquake Engineering* 9(2) June: 122–31

7.26   Mallick D V, Garg R P 1971 Effect of openings on the lateral stiffness of infilled frames. *Proceedings of the Institution of Civil Engineers* London, **49** June: 193–209

7.27   Holmes M 1961 Steel frames with brickwork and concrete infilling. *Proceedings of the Institution of Civil Engineers* London, **19** Aug: 473–8

7.28   Smith B S, Carter C 1969 A method of analysis for infilled frames. *Proceedings of the Institution of Civil Engineers* London, **44**, Sept: 31–48

7.29   Esteva L 1966 Behaviour under alternating loads of masonry diaphragms framed by reinforced concrete members. *International Symposium on the Effects of Repeated Loading of Materials and Structures*, Mexico Sept 1966 Vol 5

7.30   Fiarato A E, Sozen M A, Gamble W L 1970 *An Investigation of the Interaction of Reinforced Concrete Frames with Masonry Filler Walls* Structural Research Series No 370, University of Illinois, Nov 1970

7.31   Wood R H 1978 Plasticity, composite action and collapse design of unreinforced shear wall panels in frames. *Proceedings of the Institution of Civil Engineers* London, Part 2 **65** June: 381–411

7.32   Liauw T C, Kwan K H 1983 Plastic theory of non-integral infilled frames. *Proceedings of the Institution of Civil Engineers* London, Part 2 **75** Sept: 379–96

7.33   Liauw T C, Kwan K H 1983 Plastic theory of infilled frames with finite interface shear strength. *Proceedings of the Institution of Civil Engineers* London, Part 2 **75** Dec: 707–23

7.34   Dawe J L, Yong T C 1985 An investigation of factors influencing the behaviour of masonry infill in steel frames subjected to in-plane shear. In McNeilly T, Scrivener J C (eds) *Proceedings of the Seventh International Brick Masonry Conference* Melbourne Feb 1985 Vol 2 pp 803–14

7.35   Achytha H, Rahman S S U, Karisiddappa 1988 Effect of position of openings on the behaviour of infilled frames. In de Courcy J W (ed) *Proceedings of the Eighth International Brick/Block Masonry Conference* Dublin Sept 1988 Vol 2 pp 1108–18

8 Seismic Design of Reinforced Masonry

Professor M J N Priestley, University of California,
San Diego

Introduction — The Importance of Strength Design

Higher annual probabilities of damage are accepted under seismic loading than under other comparable extreme loads, such as maximum live load, or wind loading. Fc. example, modern seismic loading codes typically specify design earthquakes with a return period of 100–500 years for ordinary structures such as office buildings. Where seismic lateral loads are based on ductile response to the design earthquake, this can imply that the ultimate load capacity (albeit with zero or limited ductility demand) can be achieved with an expected annual probability as high as $p = 0.01–0.03$. This compares with accepted annual probabilities for achieving ultimate capacity under gravity loads of perhaps $p = 0.0001–0.001$ per year. It follows that the consequences resulting from the lack of a rational seismic design philosophy are likely to be severe.

Great advances have been made over the last 20 years in the design philosophy of reinforced concrete and steel structures responding to earthquake loading. Despite evidence provided by poor performance of masonry structures in recent earthquakes,[8.1] indicating the need for more rational design, the developments in masonry design have been less appreciable. The consequence has been that designers are often reluctant to use masonry elements in the major lateral load-resisting system in regions of high seismicity, except for minor structures. The uncertainty about performance is incorporated in many design codes[8.2,8.3] which generally stipulate elastic design to low allowable stress levels in the belief that behaviour at service load levels is more predictable than at ultimate. Elastic design for seismic loading is also intended to protect masonry structures from inelastic action, and hence hopefully from damage under code-level ground excitation.

In fact, both of these premises are highly suspect. At service load levels, the influence of shrinkage, temperature, creep and settlement will often mean that stress levels predicted by elastic theory bear little resemblance to the true stresses. Further, the 'plane sections remain plane' hypothesis may be invalid in many cases, particularly for squat masonry shear walls under in-plane loading. Ultimate strength behaviour is, however, rather insensitive to these aspects, so ultimate moments and shears can be predicted with comparative accuracy. There is now adequate test information[8.4–8.6] to support the application of ultimate strength methods developed for reinforced concrete, to reinforced masonry design.

The use of elastic design methods will not generally protect masonry structures from inelastic action under seismic loading. Consider the typical smoothed acceleration response spectra of Fig. 8.1(a),[8.7] which has been scaled to the intensity of the moderate El Centro 1940 N−S accelerogram. Masonry structures, being stiff, typically have fundamental periods in the range 0.1−0.8 s, thus spanning the frequency range of maximum response. Assuming a 5 per cent equivalent viscous damping, peak elastic response of the order of 0.8 g can be anticipated.

Design for such high lateral force levels is not economically viable, and seismic coefficients included in most codes are reduced from the elastic response levels, typically by a factor of about 4, implying considerable ductility demand, as shown in Fig. 8.1(b), since reduced strength is accompanied by increased inelastic displacement. Consequently it is to be expected that under the design-level earthquake, the structure will attain its ultimate strength, and be required to deform inelastically in a ductile manner without significant loss of strength. The equal displacement rule, illustrated in Fig. 8.1(b), implies that the maximum displacement response Δu is independent of the strength for structures of equal elastic stiffness. Thus if a masonry building is designed to allowable stress levels at the code level of lateral load, it will still attain its ultimate capacity under the design earthquake, but with a reduction in the required structure ductility factor, given by $\mu = \Delta u / \Delta y'$ in Fig. 8.1(b). In fact, for short period structures, the equal displacement principle is known to be non-conservative, and ductility demand is likely to be higher. For satisfactory seismic response, masonry structural elements providing lateral level resistance must be able to deform inelastically for several cycles without excessive strength or stiffness degradation.

Design to elastic theory in such cases is a 'head in the sand' approach, unless the structure is designed for the full lateral force level corresponding to elastic response. A more realistic approach is to accept that the ultimate capacity of the structure will be attained, and to design accordingly by ensuring that the materials and structural systems adopted are capable of sustaining the required ductility without excessive strength of stiffness degradation.

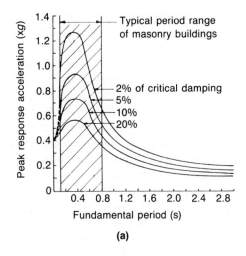

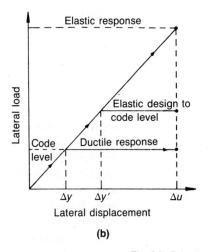

Fig. 8.1 Seismic loads for masonry structures: (a) composite response spectra from eight accelerograms scaled to El Centro 1940 N–S (after Skinner); (b) peak lateral load using 'equal displacement' principle

Choice of Structural Form

Perhaps the most basic aspect of a successful design philosophy is the choice of a suitable structural form. This will dictate the location of areas of inelastic action (plastic hinges), and the relationship between local curvature ductility demand and overall structural ductility demand.

Cantilever Shear Walls

The ductility capacity of a masonry wall will depend principally on the structural form and the ultimate curvature capacity of the wall. To ensure adequate ductility, the preferred structural form is the simple cantilever shear wall. Where two or more such walls occur in the same plane, linkage between them could be provided by flexible floor slabs (Fig. 8.2(a)) to ensure moment transfer between the walls is minimized.

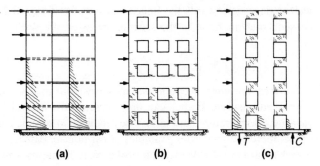

Fig. 8.2 Masonry shear wall buildings subjected to seismic forces: (a) linked cantilever walls ductile response; (b) coupled shear walls pier failure; (c) coupled shear walls spandrel failure

Openings within the wall elevation should be kept small enough to ensure that the basic cantilever action is not affected. Energy dissipation occurs only in carefully detailed plastic hinges at the base of each wall.

Traditional masonry construction has generally consisted of peripheral masonry shear walls pierced by window and door openings, as idealized in Figs 8.2(b) and (c). Under inelastic response to lateral loading, hinging may initiate in the piers (Fig. 8.2(b)) or the spandrels (Fig. 8.2(c)). In the former, and more common case, the piers will be required to exhibit substantial ductility unless designed to resist elastically the displacements resulting from the design earthquake. Plastic displacement (flexural or shear) will inevitably be concentrated in the piers of one storey, generally the lowest, with consequential extremely high ductility demand at that level. It can be shown[8.8] that for a regular wall where pier height is half the storey height, the displacement ductility factor μ_p required of the piers is related to the structure ductility demand, μ, by the expression

$$\mu_p = 2n(\mu - 1) + 1 \qquad [8.1]$$

where n is the number of storeys. Thus for a 10-storey masonry shear wall designed for $\mu = 4$, the pier ductility demand would be $\mu_p = 61$. Extensive experimental research on piers at the University of California, Berkeley[8.6] has indicated extreme difficulty in obtaining reliable ductility levels an order of magnitude lower than this value. It is concluded that the structural system of Fig. 8.2(b) is only suitable if very low structural ductilities are required.

Occasionally, openings in masonry walls will be of such proportions that spandrels will be relatively weaker than piers, and behaviour will approximate coupled shear walls, with crack patterns as illustrated in Fig. 8.2(c). Although well-detailed coupled shear walls in reinforced concrete constitute an excellent structural system for seismic resistance, diagonal reinforcement of the spandrel beams is generally necessary to satisfy the high spandrel ductility demand. Such a reinforcement system is unsuitable for structural masonry, and strength and stiffness degradation of the spandrel is likely at moderate ductilities, causing the coupled shear wall to degrade towards the linked shear walls of Fig. 8.2(a), with a consequential increase in the seismic forces on the walls.

Infilled Frames

It is a common misconception that masonry infill in structural steel or reinforced concrete frames can only increase the overall lateral load capacity, and therefore must always be beneficial to seismic performance. In fact there are numerous examples of earthquake damage that can be traced to structural modification of the basic frame by so-called non-structural masonry partitions and infill panels. Even if they are relatively

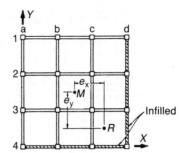

Fig. 8.3 Plan of reinforced concrete frame building with masonry infill on two boundaries: M = centre of mass; R = centre of rigidity

weak, masonry infill can drastically alter the intended structural response, attracting forces to parts of the structure which have not been designed to resist them. Two examples are illustrated below to examine this behaviour.

Consider the floor plan of a symmetrical multi-storey reinforced concrete frame building with masonry infill panels on two boundary walls, as shown in Fig. 8.3. If the masonry infill is ignored in the design phase it may be assumed that each frame in each direction (i.e. frames 1, 2, 3 and 4 in the X-direction, and frames a, b, c and d in the Y-direction) is subjected to the same seismic lateral loads, because of the structural symmetry. The true influence of the infill on frames 4 and d will be to stiffen these frames relative to the other frames. The consequence will be that the natural period of the structure will decrease, and seismic forces will correspondingly increase. Further, the *proportion* of the total seismic shear at each floor transmitted by the infilled frames will increase because of the increased stiffness of these frames relative to the other frames. The structure will also be subjected to seismic torsional response because of the shift of centre of rigidity. Thus for seismic response along the X- and Y-axes respectively, the torsional moments will be

$$X\text{-axis: } M_T = Me_y \qquad\qquad [8.2a]$$

$$Y\text{-axis: } M_T = Me_x \qquad\qquad [8.2b]$$

where M is the total floor mass.

The high shear forces generated in the infilled frames are transmitted primarily by shear stresses in the panels. Shear failure commonly results, with shedding of masonry into streets below, or into stairwells, with great hazard to life.

A second example is illustrated in Fig. 8.4, which shows masonry infill which extends for only part of the storey height, to allow for windows. Again the infill will stiffen the frame, reducing the natural period and increasing seismic forces. If the frame is designed for ductile response to the design-level earthquake, without consideration of the effect of the

Fig. 8.4 Partial
masonry infill

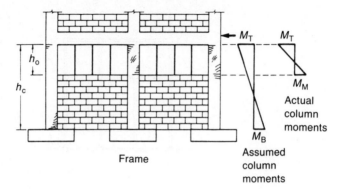

Frame

Assumed
column
moments

Actual
column
moments

infill, plastic hinges might be expected at top and bottom of columns. Because of the ductile design, these hinges would develop at a fraction of the full design-level earthquake. The influence of the infill will be to stiffen the centre and right column (for the direction of lateral load shown) causing plastic hinges to form at top of the column and top of the infill, as shown in Fig. 8.4. The consequence will be an increase in column shears. The design level of shear force in the column will be

$$V_D = \frac{M_T + M_B}{h_c} \qquad [8.3]$$

where h_c is the clear storey height. The actual shear force will be

$$V_A = \frac{M_T + M_M}{h_o} \qquad [8.4]$$

where h_o is the height of the window opening. If the column is not designed for the higher shear force of Eq. 8.4, shear failure can be expected. It should be noted that this higher shear force, corresponding to formation of plastic hinges as shown, can develop because the original design was ductile. Hence the higher shear force will be developed, but at lower ductility, as shown in Fig. 8.1(b).

When masonry infill is to be used there are two design alternatives. The designer may effectively isolate the panel from frame deformations by providing a flexible strip between the frame and panel, filled with a highly deformable material such as polystyrene. Alternatively, the designer may allow the panel and frame to be in full contact, and design both for the seismic forces to which they will be subjected. The first option, of isolation, is not very effective as it is not possible nor desirable to provide flexibility at the base of the panel, and it is difficulty to provide support against out-of-plane seismic forces.

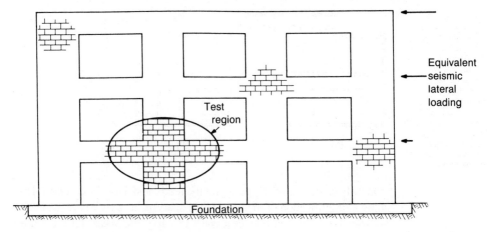

Fig. 8.5 Masonry frame building subjected to seismic forces

Masonry Frames

An alternative reinforced masonry structural system that is suitable for ductile response, is the moment-resisting frame, whose proportions in terms of the ratio of bay length to storey height is more typical of reinforced concrete frames than those of Fig. 8.2(c). Such an example is shown in Fig. 8.5. The system could be constructed from either reinforced grouted brick masonry (two leaves of solid bricks separated by a grouted and reinforced cavity) or hollow unit concrete masonry. As shown in Fig. 8.5, the column units considered are constructed using standard units, rather than special pilaster units which effectively act only as permanent formwork, and which may be suitable for smaller structures than envisaged in this chapter.

Provided such a frame is detailed in such a way as to ensure that a suitable beam-hinging mechanism is developed, with shear and column failures avoided by use of a capacity design approach, there is no reason why such a structural form should not perform well under seismic loading. This viewpoint is confirmed by test results briefly summarized later in this chapter.

Secondary Walls

Some shear wall structures do not lend themselves to rational analysis under lateral loading, as a consequence of the number, orientation and complexity of shape of the load-bearing walls. In such cases the designer may consider the walls to consist of a primary system which carries gravity loads and the entire seismic lateral load, and a secondary system

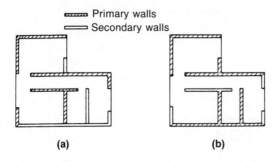

(a)   **(b)**

which is designed to support gravity loads and face loads only. This allows simplification of the lateral load analysis in cases where the extent of wall area exceeds that necessary to carry the code seismic loads. However, although it is assumed in the analysis that the secondary walls do not carry any in-plane loads, it is clear that they will carry an albeit indeterminate proportion of the lateral load. Consequently they must be detailed to sustain the deformation to which they will be subjected, by specifying similar standards as for structural walls, though code minimum requirements for reinforcement will normally be adopted. To ensure that satisfactory behaviour results, the natural period should be based on an assessed stiffness of the composite primary/secondary system.

No secondary wall should have a stiffness greater than about one-quarter that of the stiffest wall of the primary system. This is to ensure that the probability of significant inelastic deformation developing in secondary walls is minimized, and integrity of secondary walls for the role of gravity load support is maintained. Long stiff secondary walls may be divided into a series of more flexible walls by the incorporation of vertical control joints at regular centres. A further requirement in selecting the primary and secondary systems of walls is that the centres of rigidity of the two systems should be as close as possible to minimize unexpected torsional effects. Figure 8.6 shows acceptable and unacceptable division of a complex system of walls into primary and secondary systems.

Design Considerations

Ultimate Flexural Strength of Masonry Shear Walls

Compression Stress—Strain Curves for Masonry

Ultimate strength design of masonry requires knowledge of the complete compression stress—strain curve, including the crushing strength f_m, the ultimate compression strain ϵ_{cu}, and the shape of both rising and falling

Fig. 8.7 Stress–strain curves for concrete masonry[8.9]

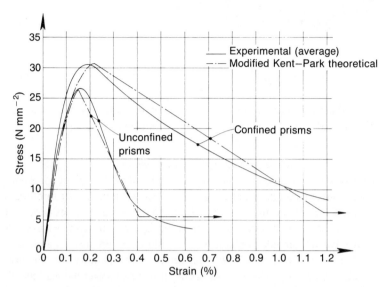

Strain (%)

branch portions of the curve. From these, the parameters defining the shape of an equivalent rectangular stress block having the same area and centroidal location as the real stress block may be found, enabling flexural strength equations similar to those deveoped by the ACI for concrete structures to be used.

Recent research[8.9] on grouted concrete masonry prisms has indicated that the stress–strain curves for masonry in compression can be represented by suitably modified equations developed for reinforced concrete. Figure 8.7 compares experimental results with theoretical curves found by modifying the Kent–Park curve for concrete.[8.9, 8.10] Results are shown for unconfined concrete masonry, and for masonry with 3 mm steel plates laid in the mortar beds to provide a degree of confinement to the masonry. It was found that the compression of unconfined masonry could be represented by a stress block defined by an average stress of $0.85f_m$, with a depth $d_c = 0.85x$ (where x is distance from the extreme compression fibre to the neutral axis) and an ultimate compression strain of $\epsilon_u = 0.0025$. For confined masonry, the corresponding values were: average stress $= 0.9F_m$, where F_m is the compression strength of confined masonry, $d_c = 0.96x$, and $\epsilon_u = 0.008$.

Recent research in the USA by Atkinson and Kingsley[8.11] has indicated similar behaviour for hollow clay brick masonry, though ultimate compression strains of about 0.003 appear to be more reasonable.

The compressioin strength of confined masonry is given by the Kent–Park enhancement factor[8.10] as

$$F_m = Kf_m \qquad\qquad [8.5]$$

where

$$K = 1 + \rho_s \frac{f_y}{f_m}. \qquad\qquad [8.6]$$

ρ_s is the volumetric ratio of confinement provided by the confining plates, and f_y is the yield stress of the confining plate material.

Distribution of Flexural Reinforcement

Using the information presented above, the flexural strength of a masonry shear wall can be calculated using the normal assumptions for reinforced concrete. It is of interest, however, to consider the influence of distribution of flexural reinforcement on flexural strength. Figure 8.8 shows two rectangular section walls of identical dimensions and axial load level, reinforced with the same total quantity of flexural reinforcement, A_{st}, which is uniformly distributed along the wall length in Fig. 8.8(a), but concentrated in two bundles of $A_{st}/2$, one at each end of the wall in Fig. 8.8(b). Elastic theory indicates that the distribution of Fig. 8.8(b) results in a moment about 33 per cent higher than for the distributed reinforcement of Fig. 8.8.(a). However, for the typically low steel percentages and low axial loads common in masonry construction, the ultimate flexural capacity is insensitive to the steel distribution. For uniformly distributed reinforcement (Fig. 8.8.(a)) the small neutral axis depth will ensure tensile yield of virtually all vertical reinforcement, resulting in an ultimate capacity of

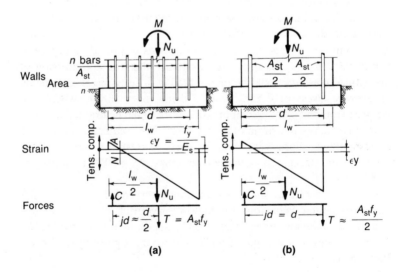

Fig. 8.8 Effect of steel distribution on flexural capacity: (a) distributed steel; (b) steel concentrated at ends

$$M_{\mathrm{u}} \approx A_{\mathrm{s}}f_{\mathrm{y}}\frac{d}{2} + N_{\mathrm{u}}\frac{l_{\mathrm{w}}}{2}. \qquad [8.7]$$

For reinforcement concentrated near the ends of the wall, the tension force, at $0.5A_{\mathrm{s}}f_{\mathrm{y}}$, is approximately half that for the distributed case, but at roughly twice the lever arm, so that flexural capacity again approximates to Eq. 8.7.

In fact there are strong reasons for adopting uniform distribution of the flexural steel along the wall when seismic loading is considered. Distributed reinforcement will result in a higher masonry flexural compression force, and therefore more efficient compression shear transfer, and provides a clamping force along the wall base joint, which is a region of potential sliding. Concentration of steel close to the wall ends results in congestion and difficulty with effective grouting, and causes high bond stresses on the limited grout area. Due to a potential for vertical splitting in the compression zone at ultimate, lateral stability provided by the masonry will often be inadequate to prevent the compression steel from buckling. This factor is less significant for walls with distributed reinforcement. Because of these factors, a recent New Zealand Masonry Design Code[8.12] requires that flexural reinforcement in shear walls be essentially uniformly distributed, and stipulates ultimate strength design.

Flexural Strength Reduction Factor

As with reinforced concrete design, a flexural strength reduction factor is necessary to allow for possible under-strength materials, dimensional errors, and inaccuracies in analysis. Values suggested for masonry shear walls[8.12] are

for $N_{\mathrm{u}} = 0$ $\phi_{\mathrm{f}} = 0.85$
for $N_{\mathrm{u}} \geq 0.1f_{\mathrm{m}}A_{\mathrm{m}}$ $\phi_{\mathrm{f}} = 0.65$

with linear variation between $\phi_{\mathrm{f}} = 0.65$ and $\phi_{\mathrm{f}} = 0.85$ as the axial load N_{u} decreases from $0.1f_{\mathrm{m}}A_{\mathrm{m}}$ to zero, where A_{m} = gross section area.

Shear Strength of Masonry Shear Walls

Design Shear Force

Since shear failure is brittle, it must be avoided for masonry structures required to exhibit ductility under seismic loading. To ensure this, the shear strength must exceed the shear corresponding to maximum feasible flexural strength. Since flexural strength will be based on nominal (and therefore generally conservative) material strengths, and a strength reduction factor of $0.65 \leq \phi_{\mathrm{f}} \leq 0.85$, the probable flexural strength will exceed the dependable strength by a substantial margin. Strain hardening of tensile reinforcement at high flexural ductilities will further enhance the flexural strength, particularly for walls reinforced with high-strength reinforcement, which typically exhibits early strain hardening. Figure 8.1 indicates that a wall designed for ductile response under seismic loading will develop its *actual* flexural strength, albeit at a lower ductility than that corresponding to dependable strength.

Consequently the maximum feasible shear V_D may be related to the shear corresponding to dependable flexural strength V_F by the relationship

$$V_D = \frac{\phi_o}{\phi_f} V_F \qquad\qquad [8.8]$$

where ϕ_o is a strength enhancement factor reflecting the influence of strain hardening, and higher than specified material strength. Typically for reinforcement with $f_y = 275 \text{ N mm}^{-2}$, $\phi_o = 1.25$ is appropriate.[8.13] For slender multi-storey shear walls, a further shear amplification factor ω_v is advisable to allow for possible variations in the ratio of shear to flexure from that corresponding to a code distribution of lateral loads, resulting from higher-mode response.[8.14] Typical values for ω_v are $1.2 \le \omega_v \le 1.8$.

Shear Carried by Masonry Shear-Resisting Mechanisms

Within potential plastic hinge regions, wide flexure–shear cracks and the effects of load reversals are likely to reduce severely the efficiency of the components contributing to masonry shear strength, namely compression shear transfer, aggregate interlock and dowel action. At present there are insufficient experimental data to quantify the reduction in shear strength of masonry with increasing ductility, though research in progress in the USA as part of the Joint US–Japan study on behaviour of masonry structures[8.15] should provide useful data in the near future. Until then the conservative assumption should be made that all shear in potential plastic hinge regions should be carried by horizontal shear reinforcement.

Two possible situations are identified in Fig. 8.9 for the design of shear reinforcement. When the aspect ratio h_w/l_w exceeds unity (Fig. 8.9(a)) a potential shear crack, inclined at $45°$, crosses the entire width of the wall. Normal reinforced concrete theory gives the required steel area A_v, at vertical spacing s, as

$$A_v = \frac{V_D s}{\phi_s f_y d} \qquad\qquad [8.9]$$

where ϕ_s is the strength reduction factor for shear, and d is the effective depth, normally taken as $0.8l_w$ for walls with distributed reinforcement.

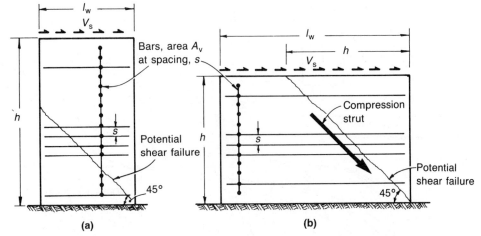

Fig. 8.9 Shear capacity of horizontal reinforcement in walls: (a) slender wall $(h/l_w > 1.01)$; (b) squat wall $(h/l_w < 1.01)$

When the aspect ratio is less than unity (Fig. 8.9(b)), the critical 45° crack intersects the wall top. Recent research on squat concrete walls[8.16] is applicable to masonry, and indicates that the shear entering the wall on the tension side of the 45° line from the compression toe can be transmitted by arch action involving the vertical flexural reinforcement, and inclined masonry compression struts. Shear reinforcement needs to be provided to transfer the shear entering the wall on the compression side of the potential inclined crack, back across the crack into the body of the wall. Thus in Fig. 8.9b, assuming that V_D is distributed evenly across the wall length, the required steel area is

$$A_v = \frac{1}{\phi_s} V_D \frac{h}{l_w} \frac{s}{f_y h_w} = \frac{V_D s}{\phi_s f_y l_w}. \qquad [8.10]$$

When the design shear force V_D in Eq. 8.9 or 8.10 is based on the capacity design approach described above, the strength reduction factor may be taken as $\phi_s = 1.0$ to avoid unnecessary conservatism. In all other circumstances, it should be taken as $\phi_s = 0.80$.[8.12]

Tests on a wide range of masonry shear walls have shown that if shear reinforcement is designed in accordance with the procedure outlined above, shear failure will be inhibited and a ductile flexural hinging mechanism will develop, even for walls with aspect ratios less than unity.

Figure 8.10 shows the load–deflection hysteresis loops for a typical squat wall of aspect ratio 0.75, tested under gradually increasing levels of displacement ductility factor. Also shown in Fig. 8.10 are the theoretical ultimate load P_u, and the first-yield load P_y, based on measured material strengths, and a strength reduction factor of $\phi_s = 1.0$. It will be seen that maximum experimental lateral loads exceeded P_u at the first peaks to $\mu = 2$ and 6. During subsequent cycles to the

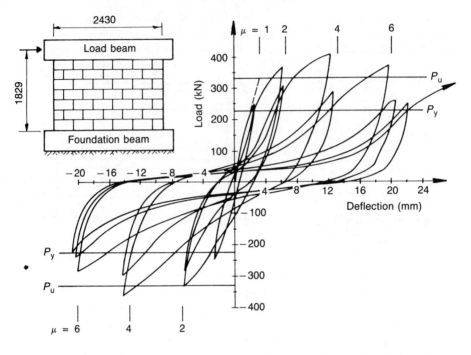

Fig. 8.10 Load–deflection behaviour of a squat concrete masonry wall

same level of displacement ductility significant load and stiffness degradation occurred as a result of a tendency of the wall to slide along the top of the foundation beam. However, on reloading to a higher level of displacement, the ultimate strength was again achieved. These results indicated that flexural failure modes with considerable ductility could be achieved from squat walls, but that energy absorption, as measured by area within the hysteresis loops, was limited by the base slip. The results are very similar to those for squat reinforced concrete walls.[8.16]

Ductility of Masonry Shear Walls

The maximum displacement, and hence the ductility capacity of a masonry structure, is a function of the ultimate curvature ϕ_u, which can be expressed as

$$\phi_u = \epsilon_u/x \qquad [8.11]$$

where ϵ_u is the ultimate compression strain, and x is the distance from the extreme compression fibre to the neutral axis.

Based on an elastoplastic approximation of the load–deflection response of cantilever shear walls, and the equivalent stress block for masonry in compression, discussed above, it is a straightforward matter to calculate the displacement ductility capacity of a wall. Recent research[8.17] supports the use of a plastic hinge length for ductility calculations that is equal to half the section length, regardless of wall aspect ratio. Adopting this value, it can be shown[8.18] that the available displacement ductility is

$$\mu = 1 + \frac{1.5}{A_e} \left(\frac{\phi_u}{\phi_y} \frac{M_y}{M_u} - 1 \right) \left(1 - \frac{1}{4A_e} \right) \qquad [8.12]$$

where A_e is the effective aspect ratio, based on height to the centre of lateral seismic force, rather than on wall height, ϕ_y is the curvature at the wall base when the extreme tension reinforcement is just as yield strain, and M_y and M_u are the base moments at first yield and ultimate respectively. Equation 8.12 indicates that μ will decrease as the aspect ratio (i.e. slenderness) of the wall increases. The other principal variable, namely the ratio of ultimate to yield curvature, ϕ_{uy}/ϕ_y, will depend on the material strengths, reinforcement ratio and axial load level.

Figure 8.11 compares ductility of cantilever shear walls of aspect ratio $A = h/l_w = 3$ with and without confining plates in the plastic hinge region.[8.18] As noted above, and illustrated in Fig. 8.7, confining plates greatly increase the effective ultimate strain (from about 0.0025 to 0.008) by inhibiting the characteristic vertical splitting failure mode. The design charts of Fig. 8.11 relate the ductility capacity μ_3 to the axial load ratio $N_u/f_m A_m$, and the non-dimensionalized reinforcement ratio, ρ'. For unconfined masonry (Fig. 8.10(a)),

$$\rho' = \rho \frac{8}{f_m} = \frac{A_{st}}{l_w t} \frac{8}{f_m} \qquad [8.13]$$

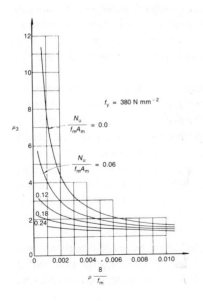

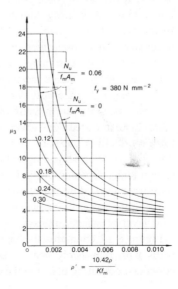

Fig. 8.11 Ductility capacity of rectangular section walls with aspect ratio $h/l_w = 3$

where A_{st} is the total area of flexural reinforcement, essentially uniformly distributed along the wall of length l_w and thickness t, and f_m is the masonry strength in N mm^{-2}.

For confined masonry (Fig. 8.11(b)) the effect of confinement on crushing strength is incorporated in the dimensionless reinforcement ratio as

$$\rho' = \frac{10.42}{Kf_m} \rho \qquad [8.14]$$

where K is given by Eq. 8.5.

Figure 8.11 indicates that displacement ductility capacity reduces as the axial load ratio or the reinforcement ratio increases, but increases as f_m increases. Comparison of Figs 8.11(a) and (b) indicates that using confining plates in plastic hinge regions can be expected to increase ductility capacity at least threefold.

The curves of Fig. 8.11 apply for walls of aspect ratio $A = 3$. By manipulation of Eq. 8.12, the ductility μ_A of a wall of aspect ratio A may be related to the ductility μ_3, given in Fig. 8.11 by the expression

$$\mu_A = 1 + \frac{3.43\,(\mu_3 - 1)\,(1 - 0.375/A)}{A} \qquad [8.15]$$

In Eq. 8.15 (and Fig. 8.11) the aspect ratio is related to the full wall height for simplicity, rather than using the effective aspect ratio of Eq. 8.12. For regular walls, $A \approx 1.5A_e$. The ductility capacity found from Fig. 8.11 (or similar charts for different yield stresses)[8.18] should be compared with that implied by the ratio of elastic response coefficient to code-level lateral force coefficient, as illustrated in Fig. 8.1(a). As noted above, a ductility demand of about $\mu = 4$ is typically implied. In the event that available ductility is less than this, redesign will be necessary. The most effective design options will be to increase f_m, increase t, or use confining plates.

In order to investigate the theoretical reduction in ductility capacity with increasing slenderness implied by Eq. 8.15, a series of tall slender concrete masonry shear walls of effective aspect ratio $A_e = 2.5$ has recently been tested.[8.5] As well as testing the influence of wall aspect ratio on ductility capacity, the walls were intended to investigate the potential for lateral buckling of the compression end of the plastic hinge region under repeated cyclic loading, the influence of lapping flexural reinforcement within the plastic hinge region at the wall base, the use of confining plates in the plastic hinge region, and the influence of axial load level of seismic response.

Figure 8.12 compares the load−deflection hysteresis loops for two walls with reasonably heavy axial load, identical except that wall 2 contained confining plates in the critical mortar beds, while wall 1 was unconfined. The confining plates in wall 2 were 600 mm long and were placed at each end of the wall, only in the bottom seven mortar courses.

During cycling of the unconfined wall to $\mu = 2.84$, crushing of mortar beds and vertical splitting of blocks within the compression zones near

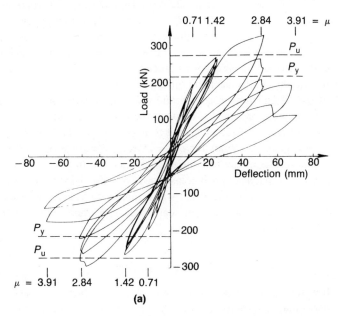

(a)

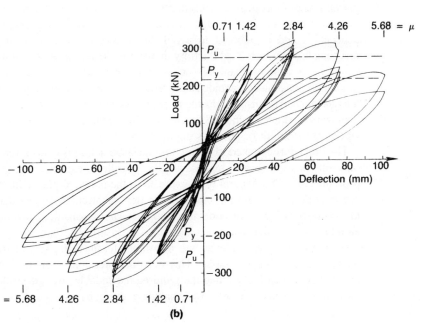

(b)

Fig. 8.12 Load–deflection behaviour of concrete masonry walls of high aspect ratio: (a) unconfined wall; (b) confined wall

the wall ends occurred. The vertical splitting, which is characteristic of the failure mechanism of masonry in compression, resulted in bond failure along the extreme tension reinforcement on reversal of load direction. This in turn caused degradation of load capacity, as is evident from the successive cycles at $\mu = 2.84$ in Fig. 8.10(a). On increasing the displacement to a ductility factor of $\mu = 3.91$, further physical and load degradation occurred and the test was abandoned.

The companion confined wall exhibited much better behaviour. At a ductility of $\mu = 2.84$ the wall exceeded the theoretical ultimate strength for each peak displacement during four complete cycles. At a ductility of $\mu = 4.26$, some cracking and crushing of individual face shells in the compression zones at the wall base occurred, but load degradation was not severe. Further testing to $\mu = 5.68$ resulted in extensive loss of face shells, and buckling of the extreme compression reinforcement.

The results of the test series confirmed the theoretical reduction in ductility capacity with increased aspect ratio. Using the design chart approach of Fig. 8.11, wall 1 was estimated to have a ductility capacity of $\mu = 2.3$, which was in reasonable agreement with the observed degradation at $\mu = 2.8$.

Design of Masonry Frames

It is now generally accepted that to obtain satisfactory inelastic seismic performance from multi-storey building frames, it is necessary to force plastic hinges to form at the ends of beams, and to avoid plastic hinging in the columns. This is the so-called weak-beam/strong-column concept[8.19] and is adopted to avoid the formation of a soft-storey mechanism with high local ductility demand on lower-storey columns. Other undesirable mechanisms such as beam or column shear failures, or joint failures, must be avoided since these are brittle, and do not possess the fundamental requisite of ductile response, namely the ability to deform inelastically during repeated cyclic displacement response without significant strength or stiffness degradation.

The procedure adopted to ensure that inelastic action is concentrated only in flexural beam hinges is the so-called 'capacity design' procedure.[8.13] The flexural reinforcement of the potential plastic hinge region is detailed to ensure a dependable flexural strength no less than that corresponding to the code distribution of lateral seismic loads, but all other parts of the structure are detailed to ensure that their strength exceeds that corresponding to the maximum feasible strength of the potential plastic hinge regions. This maximum feasible strength is of course very much higher than the required dependable strength of the beam hinges, since the latter will include a strength reduction factor,

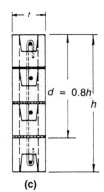

(a)

(b)

(c)

$d = 0.8h$

h

Fig. 8.13
Distribution of
beam flexural
reinforcement: (a)
reinforced
concrete; (b)
masonry
reinforcement at
maximum lever
arm, congestion
results; (c)
masonry
distributed
reinforcement,
preferred system

and be based on conservative estimates of material strengths (masonry compression strength and reinforcement yield strength) rather than actual strengths. Further, at high ductility levels, flexural reinforcement in plastic hinge regions may be strained into the strain-hardening range, resulting in reinforcement stresses which exceed the actual yield stress. This procedure recognizes that it is the actual flexural strength rather than the dependable strength that will be developed at the plastic hinges, as has already been noted above when discussing the shear design of cantilever shear walls.

Beam Flexure
As shown in Fig. 8.13(c), the beam flexural reinforcement should be uniformly distributed down the beam depth rather than attempting to follow conventional reinforced concrete beam design (Fig. 8.13(a)), which will produce excessive congestion in the typically narrow masonry beam (Fig. 8.13(c)). If hollow unit masonry is used, this will imply the use of bond-beam units at all courses.

Beam Shear
Beam shear design should be based on maximum feasible flexural strength being attained in the beam plastic hinges, and the conservative assumption that all beam shear force needs to be carried by shear reinforcement.

To ensure against column plastic hinges or shear failure, design column forces must be enhanced above the level corresponding to development of dependable flexural strength in the beams, on the same basis as for beam shear. It is advisable to enhance further the design forces to reflect possible changes from the elastic distribution of forces corresponding to the code distribution of lateral loads, resulting from dynamic higher-mode response effects. For structural frames with fundamental elastic period less than 0.7 s, which will cover most masonry buildings, a

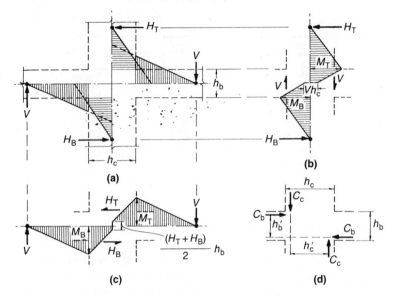

Fig. 8.14 Forces and moments for computation of joint shears: (a) forces and moments on beam column joint; (b) moments down column; (c) moments along beam; (d) flexural compression forces

dynamic amplification factor of 1.3 is appropriate.[8.19] As with shear, design to actions calculated by capacity design principles need not incorporate strength reduction factors.

Beam–column Joint Design

The design of the joint region between beams and columns requires special consideration. Two aspects are of particular importance: (1) the width of the joint (parallel to the beam axis) must be sufficient to allow the necessary change in beam reinforcement stress through the joint to be developed by bond, and (2) the dimensions and reinforcement of the joint must be adequate to carry the shear forces developed in the joint by the moment gradient across the joint.

Figure 8.14 shows the seismic forces and moments acting on a typical interior joint of a masonry frame, such as the critical region of Fig. 8.5. Because of the moment reversal across the joint, beam reinforcement may be yielding in compression at one side of the joint, and yielding in tension on the other side (Fig. 8.14(c)). Consequently the joint width, which is equal to the column width h_c, must be at least equal to the sum of tension and compression development lengths for the reinforcement. Typically this will require joint widths of

$$h_c \geq 90d_b \qquad\qquad [8.16]$$

where d_b is the diameter of the beam flexural reinforcement.

The moment gradient horizontally and vertically through the joint also enables the joint shear forces to be calculated. The relevant forces and moments for computation of the horizontal joint shear force V_{sh} are shown in Fig. 8.14(b). Note that the moment Vh'_c from the beams shear forces (assumed equal in this example) assist in effecting the change in column moment from M_T at the top of the joint to M_B at the bottom of the joint, and hence the horizontal joint shear will be

$$V_{jh} = \frac{(M_T + M_B - Vh'_c)}{h'_b}. \qquad [8.17]$$

Conventional reinforced concrete joint design theory would require all of V_{jh} to be carried by horizontal joint reinforcement in the form of stirrups unless column axial load levels are high. Thus the required area of horizontal joint reinforcement, of yield strength f_{yh} parallel to the beam reinforcement, will be

$$A_{jh} = V_{jh}/f_{yh}. \qquad [8.18]$$

Similar calculations are necessary to determine the amount of vertical joint shear reinforcement, as has been explained in detail elsewhere.[8.20]

Ductility

Inherent in the approach suggested above is the need to provide adequate ductility in the beam plastic hinges. No unique expression equivalent to Eq. 8.12 for cantilever shear walls is possible for masonry frames, as the relative contribution to elastic deformation from beams, columns and joint deformation depend on the overall frame geometry as well as beam and column section properties, while the inelastic deformation is dependent only on the plastic rotation of the beam hinges. However, based on the approximation that beam elastic deformation contributes 50 per cent to the total yield displacement, the following expression, limiting the depth of the compression zone, x, in the beam plastic hinges will ensure adequate ductility without exceeding the ultimate compression strain of $\epsilon_{cu} = 0.0025$:

$$x \leq 1.2h_b^2/(\mu l_n) \qquad [8.19]$$

where h_b is the beam depth, l_n is the clear beam span between column faces, and μ is the required structure displacement ductility factor.

Figure 8.15 shows details of a full-size reinforced masonry beam—column joint representing the region between column contraflexure points and beam contraflexure points circled in Fig. 8.5, and designed to the above principles. The general test set-up is shown in Fig. 8.15, and details of the reinforcement in Fig. 8.15. In this figure, the nomenclature 4D20 means four deformed bars of nominal diameter 20 mm and yield strength 275 N mm^{-2} etc.

Lateral load—displacement hysteresis loops for the test units are plotted in Fig. 8.15. Also included in this figure are the theoretical ultimate lateral

Fig. 8.15 Testing
of a concrete
masonry beam-
column joint: (a)
test set-up; (b)
dimensions and
reinforcement: (c)
lateral load
displacement
hysteresis loops

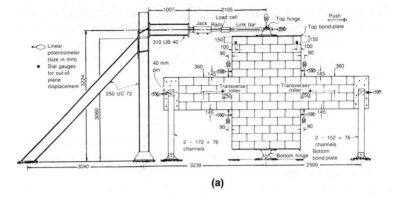

(a)

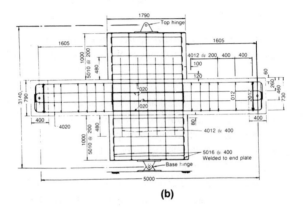

(b)

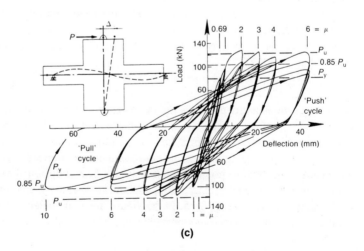

(c)

load of $P_u = 121$ kN, the theoretical load P_y at which the extreme tension rebar in the beams first reached yield stress, and the design 'dependable' strength, $0.85P_u$.

Very satisfactory performance is indicated by Fig. 8.15(c). Initial peak loads at $\mu = 2$, 3 and 4 are within ± 5 per cent of P_u, and load degradation during subsequent cycles at a given ductility level is comparatively minor. The loop shape is very stable, and indicates good energy dissipation capacity. At $\mu = 6$, the initial peak load exceeds P_u, but significant degradation occurs during the subsequent cycles, as a result of the physical degradation of the compression zones, and consequent buckling of the beam reinforcement.

The behaviour represented by Fig. 8.15(c) is as good as could be expected of well-designed reinforced concrete elements.

Detailing

It could be argued that sound detailing is even more important than the provision of adequate shear and flexural strength. It is beyond the scope of this chapter to deal with this topic in depth, and in consequence, only brief notes on matters of prime importance are included. These are based on requirements included in the recent New Zealand Masonry Design Code.[8.12]

Wall Slenderness Ratios

Within plastic hinge regions, there is a danger of lateral instability of the wall if the ratio of clear storey height to wall thickness is too high. This ratio should not exceed 13.3 unless the structure is less than three storeys high, or has a flexural compression zone (under combined axial load and bending moment) shorter than $x = 0.3l_w$ or $x = 4t$ where l_w and t are the wall length and thickness respectively. This requirement is to prevent buckling of the compression end of the wall under inelastic cycling.

Reinforcement Ratio

The sum of the horizontal and vertical reinforcement ratios for walls must be at least 0.2 per cent, which can be divided up to 2/3, 1/3 in the two directions. Maximum reinforcement ratio is related to the cavity size, and must not exceed $\rho = 8/f_y$ (or $13/f_y$ at laps) at any part of the wall. Bar diameter must not exceed 1/4 of the cavity width. Maximum spacing between adjacent bars in both horizontal and vertical directions varies with the seismicity of the site and the importance of the building, and in the most stringent case is 400 mm each way. An exception to the requirement for two-way reinforcement is made for minor structures in the less seismically active regions of New Zealand, provided the structures are designed for the elastic response levels of seismic lateral force, and are subject to design shear stress which does not exceed the appropriate value for masonry shear mechanisms in which case horizontal reinforcement may be omitted.

Anchorage

Where possible, the designer should be encouraged to avoid lapping reinforcement within plastic hinge regions. Basic development lengths of $40d_b$ and $54d_b$ are recommended for bars of diameter d_b and yield strength 275 and 380 N mm^{-2} respectively. These should be increased by 50 per cent where lapping within the plastic hinge region cannot be avoided. It should be noted that tests on unconfined slender walls indicate that even with this length of lapping, bond failure will eventually occur. The purpose of the increased lap length is to defer the bond failure for sufficient length of time to allow the structure successfully to 'ride out' the earthquake.

Non-structural Walls

Veneers and partitions, though considered non-structural, must be carefully designed to avoid the possibility of their collapse causing hazard to life. Sufficient separation between partitions and the structure's lateral load-resisting system must be provided to prevent contact during the design-level earthquake. This is to avoid loading of the partitions, and structural modification of the primary seismic system. Partitions should be reinforced to provide sufficient out-of-plane load capacity to withstand self-inertia response.

Shedding of poorly connected masonry veneer into streets during earthquakes is a real hazard to life. On multi-storey buildings, veneer should be vertically reinforced, and adequately tied back to the structural system with connections capable of allowing adequate relative lateral movement.

References

8.1   Jennings P C (ed) 1971 *Engineering Features of the San Fernando Earthquake, Feb. 9, 1971* Report EERL 71−02, California Institute of Technology, June 1971, 512pp

8.2   ACI Committee 531 1981 *Building Code Requirements for Concrete Masonry Structures (ACI 531–79)* (Revised 1981) and Commentary American Concrete Institute, Detroit 60pp

8.3   National Bureau of Standards 1978 *Tentative Provisions for the Development of Seismic Regulations for Buildings* Special Publication No 510, Washington DC pp 111–66

8.4   Priestley M J N 1977 Seismic resistance of reinforced concrete masonry shear walls with high steel percentages. *Bulletin, New Zealand National Society for Earthquake Engineering (Wellington)* **10**(1) March: 1–16

8.5   Priestley M J N, Elder D M 1982 Cyclic loading tests of slender concrete masonry shear walls. *Bulletin, New Zealand National Society for Earthquake Engineering (Wellington)* **15**(1) March: 3–21

8.6   Mayes R L, Omoto Y, Clough R W 1976 *Cyclic Shear Tests of Masonry Piers* University of California, Berkeley, Report EERC 76–8, May 1976, 84pp

8.7   Skinner R I 1964 *Earthquake Generated Forces and Moments in Tall Buildings* Department of Scientific and Industrial Research (Wellington) Bulletin No 166, 106pp

8.8   Priestley M J N 1980 Seismic design of masonry buildings — background to the Draft Masonry Design Code DZ 4210. *Bulletin, New Zealand National Society for Earthquake Engineering* **13**(4): 329–46

8.9   Priestley M J N, Elder D M 1983 Stress–strain curves for unconfined and confined concrete masonry. *ACI Journal, Proceedings* **80**(3) May/June: 192–201

8.10   Scott B D, Park R, Priestley M J N 1982 Stress–strain behaviour of concrete confined by overlapping hoops at low and high strain rates. *ACI Journal, Proceedings* **79**(1) Jan/Feb: 13–27

8.11   Atkinson R H, Kingsley G R 1985 *A Comparison of the Behavior of Clay and Concrete Masonry in Compression* US–Japan Coordinated Program for Masonry Building Research, Report 1, 1–1, Atkinson–Noland Ass, Boulder 151pp

8.12   Standards Association of New Zealand 1984 *Code of Practice for Masonry Design* NZS 4203P, Wellington

8.13   Park R, Paulay T 1975 *Reinforced Concrete Structures* John Wiley & Sons, New York 769pp

8.14   Blakeley R W G, Cooney R C, Megget L M 1975 Seismic shear loading at flexural capacity in cantilever wall structures. *Bulletin, New Zealand National Society for Earthquake Engineering* **8**(4) Dec: 278–90

8.15   Noland J L 1984 *US Research Plan* US–Japan Coordinated Program for Masonry Building Research, Atkinson–Noland Ass, Boulder 22pp

8.16   Paulay T, Priestley M J N, Synge A J 1982 Ductility of earthquake resisting squat shear walls. *ACI Journal, Proceedings* **79**(4) July/Aug: 257–69

8.17   Priestley M J N, Park R 1984 *Strength and Ductility of Bridge Substructures* RRU Bulletin 71, National Roads Board, Wellington 120pp

8.18   Priestley M J N 1981 Ductility of unconfined and confined concrete masonry shear walls. *Masonry Society Journal* **1**(2), July/Dec: T–28 to T–39

8.19 Standard Association of New Zealand 1982 *Code of Practice for the Design of Concrete Structures* NZS 3101

8.20 Priestley M J N, Chai Yuk Hon 1985 Seismic design of reinforced concrete masonry moment resisting frames. *The Masonry Society Journal* **5**(1) Jan/June

Author Index

Subject Index

This book is to be returned on or before
the last date stamped below.

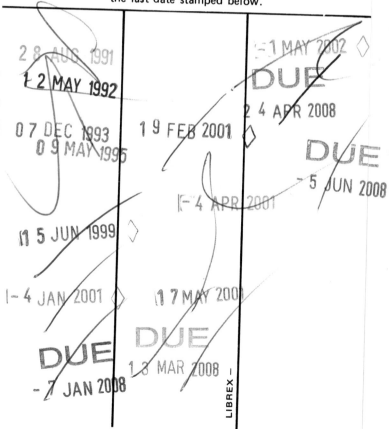